BOOK 4

THE COMPLETE SINGING RESOURCE FOR PRIMARY SCHOOLS

Val Whitlock & Shirley Court

Boosey & Hawkes Music Publishers Ltd
www.boosey.com

Acknowledgements

Amani Utupe (2-part mixed) words and music by Patsy Ford Simms © 1999 Alfred Publishing Co, Inc.
All rights reserved including public performance. Used by permission.
Hats words and music by Hank Beebe copyright © 1985 by Hal Leonard Corporation.
International copyright secured. All rights reserved.
Night Riders © copyright 2008 by Alan Simmons Music, PO Box 7, Scissett, Huddersfield HD8 9YZ,
www.alansimmonsmusic.com
Shoes © copyright 2007 by Faber Music Limited. All rights reserved. Printed by permission.
Surf, Surfin' On the Internet © copyright 2007 by Up4itmusic. Reproduced by permission of Ian Blick and Tony Brown
(up4itmusic.co.uk)
All other works © copyright 2008 Boosey & Hawkes Music Publishers Ltd

Piano accompaniment to *Singing the Greens* arranged by Christopher Hussey

Stage Songs commissioned by Val Whitlock for Solihull Massed Choir at the Schools' Prom 2005, Royal Albert Hall, with
arrangements by Ian Blick

Recording credits
Singers: Adele Bailey, Jess Glaisher, Susan Glaisher, Jon Laird, Andrew Milburn, Val Whitlock
CBSO Junior Choir (directed by Shirley Court)
Songsquad (directed by Val Whitlock)
CDs arranged and produced by Andrew Holdsworth, Method and Madness Music

Published by Boosey & Hawkes Music Publishers Ltd
Aldwych House
71–91 Aldwych
London
WC2B 4HN

www.boosey.com

© Copyright 2008 by Boosey & Hawkes Music Publishers Ltd

ISMN 979-0-060-11897-5
ISBN 978-0-85162-5171

Second impression, with corrections 2009.

Printed in England by The Halstan Printing Group Ltd, Amersham, Bucks

Notesetting by The Note Factory and Robin Hagues

Illustrations by Paul Russell

Foreword

The *Singing Sherlock* series is a firm favourite of singing leaders throughout the land and deservedly too. I have seen Val Whitlock and Shirley Court weave their wonderful magic with young singers on many occasions and so it does not surprise me at all that they have come up with yet another terrific collection of songs with equally terrific notes and ideas to go with them.

They know their stuff and they know that some teachers will feel confident in leading their young singers while others – probably the majority – are scared of taking the plunge.

What makes *Singing Sherlock* such a valuable resource is that it gives every possible encouragement and support to the latter group with real hands-on, tried and tested tips, clues and tricks (that sounds like a song title!).

What's more, there is a well devised sense of progression from simple singing games to more demanding part songs through the book. There is nothing patronising or glib about their approach though, and what shines out from the pages of this volume is a shared passion for the fun and reward of class singing.

I am particularly impressed to see the song *Tramps' Paradise* by Alice Higgins and Martha Wiltshire who were only 11 years old when they wrote it. I'd better watch out for my job!

Howard Goodall, composer & broadcaster
National Ambassador for Singing

Ideal for use with *Sing Up* and *Wider Opportunities* class singing programmes in the UK, *Singing Sherlock* also fits with DCFS/QCA Schemes of Work for Music – ongoing skills.

The Authors

Val Whitlock

Val is renowned for her infectious enthusiasm, energy and ability to motivate people about singing. She works part-time as a choral and vocal specialist for Solihull Music Service and also as a freelance workshop leader, choral director, voice consultant and author. She is in demand nationally to lead choral workshops, often involving hundreds of young people. Val has directed numerous high-profile concerts in prestigious venues; in November 2005 she directed, to wide acclaim, a massed choir of 550 Solihull children at *Music for Youth*'s *Schools' Prom*, held at the Royal Albert Hall. She currently directs two choirs for Solihull Music Service – *Songsquad*, and its training choir *The Rookies*.

Val also leads training courses for music services, national music organisations and universities, as well as acting as consultant on various national singing initiatives. She regularly adjudicates and presents events for *Music for Youth*.

Shirley Court

Shirley is nationally known for her ability to motivate and inspire young singers of all ages and capabilities. In September 2006 she was awarded with an Honorary Degree (DMus) for her work with youth choirs and her contribution to music in schools from the University of Leicester.

She regularly conducts massed choirs of primary school children for different local authorities and also for events such as *Music for Youth*'s *Schools' Prom* at the Royal Albert Hall. She is also a regular presenter of *Music for Youth*'s *Primary Proms*, both in Birmingham and in Chester.

Shirley is the conductor of both the Senior and Junior CBSO Youth Choruses. In this capacity she has worked alongside many world-famous conductors preparing the Youth Choruses for prestigious events. She has recently been appointed as conductor of the Hallé children's choir beginning in September 2008.

Currently Shirley works part-time for Cheshire Music Partnership as part of the Cheshire Vocal Strategy and is the Director of the Cheshire Youth Choir and Macclesfield Silkworms. Shirley also acts as a consultant on many national singing initiatives and runs regular vocal inset courses for teachers.

Word sheets

Word sheets for all the songs in this book are available to download from:
www.boosey.com/resources

Contents

Singing Sherlock investigates ...

... and solves the mystery of how to get children to sing well ...

Follow the clues ...

Hi! I'm
Singing Sherlock

- *I watch and listen to you carefully*
- *I ask questions to help you sing better*
- *Can you take a turn at being Singing Sherlock too?*

and check out the case notes ...

SHERLOCK'S
CASE NOTES

Investigate:

- *Background to the song*
- *How to teach the song*
- *What to expect from the children*
- *Points to look out for*

... but first ...

Do your groundwork!

PRIORITY

Know your starting point – one size does not fit all

It is important that you know the musical and vocal stage of your children. Each group you work with will have different needs – musically, vocally and socially. You will therefore have different expectations of the children, depending on their experience. Children's voices develop at different rates – psychological factors can impede progress: for example, a shy child may lack the self-confidence to project his/her voice. For children who have done very little singing it may be enough that they join in enthusiastically and co-operatively. Some children, even as old as Year 6, may still have problems pitch-matching. Other children may sing confidently and you will want to stretch them by improving their vocal tone, singing with different vocal qualities and developing their skill in part-singing.

Choose the right song

The songs in each section are grouped in *approximate* order of difficulty. However, the songs in the *Clued In* section and *Sherlock in Concert* are the most demanding musically and vocally. Many of the songs, however, can be sung in unison if the children are not yet experienced at part-singing. When planning a singing session choose a balance of songs, mixing more difficult songs with easier ones, and varying the moods and musical styles.

A singing school is a happy school

Make singing a daily activity. Sing with your class, with several year groups together and sing with the whole school. It should be vibrant and fun but above all it should be quality singing. The better the *quality*, the more pleasurable and satisfying it will be for the children, the teacher and audience.

How you teach the song is really important!

PRIORITY

Learn the song yourself

Do not attempt to teach the song before you know it well yourself. Prepare thoroughly – listen to the CD and sing along, play or sing using the music – whichever is most comfortable for you. Even if you do not plan to use the CD backing tracks in your singing session, listening to the CD will give you a good idea of how the songs should be performed.

Set the scene

You need space to sing. Singing is a very physical activity, so children need space to move their bodies freely and without tension. Be aware that desks can act as a barrier, so it is worth moving these to the side of the room to create a singing area.

When sitting to sing, it is preferable to use chairs. However, if this is not possible – for example, if the whole school is singing together in the hall – then vary the amount of time they sit and stand on the floor. If the session includes a variety of vocal activities as well as movement the children will not notice how long they are on their feet.

Children need a good singing example

The best way to teach a song to children is by using your *own* voice. When they are learning to sing, children will pitch more accurately from a human voice than from any other instrument or CD track.

However, if you are not a confident singer you can use the backing CDs, but always remember children will respond to *your* enthusiasm. For some of the simpler songs, you can invite one of the children to help you lead or, if you are able to, enlist the help of another adult who is a more confident singer, even if only occasionally.

For some songs it may be an idea first to talk about the background of the song.
Always aim for a stimulating and positive environment where the energy level is high and the activities are interesting so that the children never lose interest or motivation.

Teaching the song by singing yourself

- Sing through the song, or a verse of the song, to show how it goes.

- Use a call and response method, *eg* sing a phrase and ask the children immediately to sing back. Add a phrase at a time, then put two phrases together and gradually build up the song.

- The children will memorise the songs more quickly this way and consequently will sing with more confidence and enjoyment. Always give them a digestible amount to sing back. You will also be able to demonstrate phrasing (musical sentences), breathing and dynamics (loud and soft singing) in this way.

- If you feel confident, you can also show the shape of the melody with your hands as you sing. This is called *patterning*, and it can help the children see when the melody is getting higher or lower, and help pinpoint any intervals between notes that the children are finding difficult.

- Remember when teaching a song, you are not only teaching the notes but also teaching children *how* to sing it and *how* to use their voice. The more understanding you have of your voice as an instrument the better you will be able to communicate this to the children.

- Maintain a good pace throughout the singing session, so that the children do not get bored and lose interest. Remember, talk less – sing more.

- Try not to sing yourself when the children sing back a phrase so that you can listen for wrong notes or other insecurities.

- Always sort out any mistakes the children make *as they first happen*. Once faults have become established they are difficult and sometimes impossible to correct. Try singing the phrase again, or highlight the difficult passage using nonsense words like *Na na na* or *Doo doo doo*, or perhaps sing the phrase in a different kind of voice. If you make it humorous the children will catch on quickly.

- Another device is a game called *My Turn, Your Turn*. In this activity, the teacher/leader points to him/herself whilst singing a chosen line of the song. The teacher/leader then stops at a particular word in the song and points to the children. The children then have to sing back the next word with the correct note. This helps the children to listen really carefully.

Are you ready? Off we go!

- When teaching a song always remember to give a starting note, and count the children in. You may sing "1, 2, 3, 4" or "Are you ready? Off we go …" on the starting note. You could also use a recorder or a tuned instrument to sound the note.

- However you do it you need to indicate whether the song is in two, three or four time.

- The starting note and count in are stated at the beginning of each song in this book.

Using the CD to teach the song

- When using the CD to teach the song, do not be tempted merely to play the CD and ask the children to sing along in the hope that they will simply 'pick up' the tune. In practice what often happens is that many children can end up learning the tune, or sections of the tune, quite inaccurately and these mistakes will be almost impossible to correct afterwards.

- Play through the song once, so that the children hear how it goes.

- Next, play through the song again, but this time ask the children to join in with any repeated parts of the song or any simple actions.

- Continue in this way, putting the song together by learning short sections until it is completely familiar to the children.

- It is important that the children can hear themselves when they sing, so be careful not to allow the CD track to drown the children's voices.

Section 1 –
Voice Gym and Tune-up

Songs

Performance Backing

Warm-ups

Energise your body

The larynx is part of the body's whole muscular system, and therefore the entire body should be involved in the process of singing. Just as athletes warm up their muscles before a race, singers need to warm up both the body and the vocal folds before singing. A good warm-up also helps get rid of any tension in the body so it should always be fun. Songs and warm-ups that involve actions help release the voice and focus attention.

Whacky numbers

Punch air vigorously eight times with your right hand, then eight times with your left hand, and then kick air eight times with your right foot then eight times with your left foot. Count out loud as you perform the actions.

Repeat the sequence, but halve the numbers, *eg* four times with each hand and foot, then twice with each hand and foot, then once with each hand and foot. Finish the whole sequence by jumping in the air, arms held high in a V-shape and shout "Hey!"

Repeat the cycle again, but this time perform it with a whispering voice. The final "hey" should also be whispered.

Repeat the cycle for a final time, but this time use a thinking voice (lip-synching or 'air singing'). Do not forget the final "hey" is mimed.

Shake it off

Plunge your hands into an imaginary bowl of water. Now shake your hands vigorously to get rid of all the water. You have a sudden attack of nerves, and your knees shake uncontrollably. Now you realise you must have ants in your pants, and you shake your bottom wildly to stop the tickling. Can you do all three together?

Fruit face

Jump with your arms out wide, making big fists. Make your face really big too, whilst saying "Big pumpkin face" rather like a caveman. Now screw your face up saying "Tiny little raisin face" in a very high voice, jumping back with feet together and arms by your side.

Glove puppet

Imagine you are operating a glove puppet. As you open and close the puppet's mouth with your hand, copy the action with your own mouth as the children say the words "Yah, yah, yah, yah, yah". Repeat with 'jah' and 'bah' etc. Your jaw should be loose and floppy as you make the sounds. Use your high voice and your low voice.

Strike the right pose – good singing posture

The body supports the voice, so standing or sitting badly will affect the quality of the sound.

Standing to sing

- Stand with your feet slightly apart and no wider than your shoulders with your knees loose.

- Make sure that your shoulders are down and your arms loose and free at your side.

- Pull your shoulders up to your ears then, as you drop them down, let out a whispered "Wow". Let your eyes feel wide and your face open.

- Your neck should be free from tension and your head feeling as if it is floating above your body.

- Feel poised, standing tall and proud.

Sitting to sing

- Always sit tall even when sitting on the floor.

- Imagine that your neck is long like a giraffe.

- Make sure that you have enough space between you and the next person.

- If you are sitting on chairs make sure that there is space between them.

- Sit well back in the chair with your feet on the floor so that you can stand up immediately when required to.

Breathing

If you say to children "Take a big breath …" 99% of them will take a very high breath into the top part of the chest and you will notice their shoulders rise. Efficient breathing for singing requires a low breath into the bottom part of the lungs, and then practising how to manage (control) the breath.

The low down

- Gently blow out air as far as you can. When you feel you can not get rid of any more air relax your tummy, and notice that you will take in air automatically through your nose.

- Now try exactly the same thing, but this time open your mouth as you relax your tummy. You should feel the air cold at the back of your throat.

Buzzing bee

- Exhale on *sss* or *zzz* sounds, like a buzzing bee. Try short separate breaths to *sss* counting *1, 2, 3, 4* and then a long *sss* on *5, 6, 7, 8*.

- Try putting several sounds together *ff, tt, ff, tt* or *ss hh ff tt*.

- Put your hands on your tummy and feel your muscles kicking to help you make the sounds.

Open your throat

In order for the voice not to sound 'tight' or strained the throat needs to be open and unconstricted.

Suprise, suprise!

- Imagine someone has just given you the most amazing present. As you open the box you take a little inward breath making a silent "Ah!" Feel the cold air at the back of your throat, and a very open feeling. Now try and get the same sensation without taking the in-breath, but still feeling that your throat is really open.

Silent laugh

- You can get the same feeling by silently laughing. Imagine that you are sitting at the back of the classroom, and your friend has made you laugh but you do not want the teacher to hear …

Tongue workout

The tongue is a large, strong muscle that is very important for singing (and indeed speaking). Like any muscle it needs a good workout to function at its best. The tongue needs to be free and nimble so that words are clear.

Stick it out

- Stick your tongue out as far as it will go.

- Can you touch your nose with your tongue? If not, just see how far it will go!

- Now touch your chin with your tongue.

- Now, still with your tongue sticking out, can you move it from side to side without moving your jaw?

- How fast can you go?

Tongue rolls

- With your mouth closed roll your tongue around your mouth four times to the right and four times to the left.

- Pretend to chew a very sticky toffee, or a big piece of pink bubblegum.

Consonant code

- Make the sounds of different consonants and feel where the effort is in the tongue *eg "t t t t"* or *"d d d d"* at the front tip of tongue; *"g g g g"* or *"k k k k"* at the back of the tongue.

Voice stretch

Using the full vocal range – understanding voice registers

Many songs will be out of children's reach unless they can use their full vocal range safely and effectively. They can very easily get stuck in the lower end of their voice and sing using only inflected speech. This may be because they have never had the opportunity to explore their own voice or have never been shown ways to do this.

In very simple terms the voice has two registers, which can loosely be described as 'sections' of a voice: the lower part of the voice (sometimes called *chest voice*) and the higher part (sometimes called *head voice*).

It is crucial to help children access their higher range. As the voice goes higher (around the note F above middle C) it needs to make an adjustment, rather like changing gear. In fact, what happens is the larynx needs to tilt forward. This is not as complicated as it sounds! To make this happen, ask the children to imitate the sound of a puppy whining outside a window, wanting you to let him in, or to throw an imaginary mud pie and make a "Woah" sound at the top of your voice. (See also page 12 *Bungee Jumping* or *Lassos*.)

Children should use this part of the voice regularly. They need to learn how to make a safe, healthy sound in this register, otherwise they will always find many songs too high, or their singing will feel and sound strained. A word of caution: sitting children too close to an overhead projector or whiteboard to read song words, or too close to the teacher/leader, will cause them to stick their chins up. This prevents the larynx from tilting, making it virtually impossible to sing higher pitches comfortably and safely.

Using different vocal qualities

Just as in painting you can create many different colours and shades that express a mood, so too the human voice can create a palette of many different vocal 'colours'.

For example:

- Sing as if you are speaking (called speech quality). You will hear this quality in pop and music theatre songs. If you try to sing too high, however, it will feel very uncomfortable and sound shouted and strained. This is the point where you need to open up the next section of the voice – and allow the larynx to tilt.

- Tilting makes the sound sweeter. You can make this sound rounder or darker by singing like a politician (or Pavarotti). This quality is often used in classical singing.

- Pop, country music and music theatre singing also uses a twangy sound. At its most extreme it can sound very brassy and unrefined. Try singing like a wicked witch or miaow like a cat!

- For a particular vocal effect you can use a whispered, airy sound (called aspirate singing). *NB* Use this quality sparingly! Try singing like a princess.

You can use these vocal qualities to give 'colour' to the songs. The song *Changing Channels* (on page 20) includes several of these. The warm-ups in this section will stretch the voice as well as explore these vocal qualities.

Fireworks

This is great for accessing the higher range in the voice and making you aware of the muscles in your body that you need to help you sing.

- Make a *"vv"* sound with your bottom lip close to your top teeth. You should make a sound like a firework. Start as low in your voice as you can, slide up as high as you can and back down again.

- Make your hands into fists and place them on each side of your waist. As you make the sound do you feel the muscles kicking under your hands?

Horses and deep sea divers

- Blow air through really loose lips, making a sound rather like a horse.

- Now add your voice by making a lip-shiver or trill with a "Brr" sound.

- Try going up and down gently with this sound, keeping the air really even. See how high you can go!

- As with *Fireworks*, if you put your fists on each side of your waist you will feel the muscles working.

Jolly Santa

Imagine you are Santa Claus, and make the shape of Santa's round tummy with your arms. Now imitate Santa's jolly "Ho, ho, ho!" with your voice.

Posh Lady

Imagine you are a posh person or a politician and say "How do you do?" in a very refined voice.

Lassos

Imagine you are a cowboy on an American ranch about to catch a bull with your lasso. Pretend to throw your lasso, and call out "Yee-hi!" with a high, twangy voice. You catch your imaginary bull first time, and so you punch your fist and call out "Yo" in a deep voice.

Bungee jumping

Say "Weeeh!" starting as high in your voice as you can and sliding down as low as your voice will go.

Ear cleaning

Develop your thinking voice

Singing numbers

1. Sing up and down a five-note scale, *eg*

1,   2,   3,   4,   5.   5,   4,   3,   2,   1

2. Try missing out a note, *eg* sing 1, miss out 2, and then sing 3, 4 and 5. Make sure you hear the missing note, *eg* 2, in your head with your thinking voice before you sing the other notes. Now try singing 1, miss out (*ie think*) 2, sing 3, miss out (*think*) 4, and sing 5.

3. Try the same activity with a complete scale.

1,   2,   3,   4,   5,   6,   7,   8(1)   8(1),   7,   6,   5,   4,   3,   2,   1.

Now try singing the following:

1,   2,   1,   3,   1,   4,   1,   5,   5,   4,   5,   3,   5,   2,   5,   1

4. Ask five children to stand at the front of the group, each holding a card with a number on it. The leader points to a child, who then sings the correct note 1, 2, 3, 4 or 5.

Individuals can come to the front and make up their own little tune, indicating their choice of notes by how many fingers they hold up. The rule is they have to begin and end with note number 1.

5. Hold up your hand and use it to represent the five-line stave. Your fingers are the lines, and the spaces in-between your fingers represent the spaces on the stave. You could also ask the children to think of a ladder and explain that the rungs are like the lines of the stave, and the spaces in between the rungs are where the notes fit.

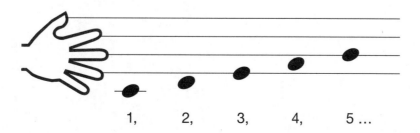

1,   2,   3,   4,   5 ...

Grand Old Duke of York

performance – CD 1 track 1; backing – CD 1 track 2
starting note – B; introduction – 3 beats

Traditional

Count in: 1 2 3

Oh, the Grand Old Duke of York, he had ten thous-and men, he
marched them up to the top of the hill and he marched them down a - gain. And
when they were up they were up, and when they were down they were down, and
when they were on - ly half - way up they were nei - ther up nor down.

Singing Sherlock wants to know:

🔍 When using your thinking voice and performing the actions, are you making sure you sing all the other words with the correct notes?

🔍 Is everyone using their singing voice, instead of their shouting voice?

🔍 Can you think of an action for the Grand Old Duke of York, eg *is he an old Duke with a walking stick, or is he a very important Royal Duke? Can you match your vocal sound to your action?*

🔍 Can you march in time on the spot as you sing and still manage to do the actions?

SHERLOCK'S CASE NOTES

- *This song works in the same way as* Heads, Shoulders, Knees and Toes, *and helps children to use their 'thinking voice'.*

- *Sing through the song to make sure all the children know this traditional tune.*

- *Sing the song adding the following actions: clap above the head on the word "up" and stamp on the word "down".*

- *Sing the song and substitute the word "up" with a clap above the head.*

- *Sing the song and substitute the word "down" with a stamp.*

- *Sing the song, replacing the words "up" and "down" with a clap and stamp.*

Toboggan

performance – CD 1 track 3; backing – CD 1 track 4
starting note – C; introduction – 4 beats

Words traditional

Count in:

1   2   1   2

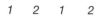

To be - gin to to - bog - gan first buy a to - bog - gan, but don't buy too big a to -

- bog-gan.   Too big a to - bog-gan is   not a to - bog-gan to   buy to be - gin to to - bog-gan.

Singing Sherlock wants to know:

- Are you speaking the rhyme clearly using your lips and your tongue?

- Are you communicating the meaning of the words rather than just chanting them?

- Are you giving each line of the rhyme the same amount of energy when you speak and sing?

- Are you listening to each other when performing the rhyme in a round?

SHERLOCK'S CASE NOTES

- Learn this first as a chant.
  (Chants are a valuable link between using the talking voice and developing the singing voice.)

- To help the children feel the rest between the first and second line of the rhyme add a clap or finger click.

- Try using a variety of different voices, eg posh, fairy or twangy like an American cowboy. Give the children opportunities to choose which voice to use.

- Now chant the rhyme in a two-part round, with the second group entering at the place marked ❷ in the music. When the children are confident you can try chanting a four-part round.

- Next, sing the rhyme to a descending scale.

- Before singing in rounds, make sure the children can sing in unison confidently and clearly.

- To develop their listening skills ask each group of children to face each other as they sing in rounds.

Here Comes Sally

performance – CD 1 track 5; backing – CD 1 track 6
starting note – C; introduction – 8 beats

Traditional

Count in: 1 2 3 4

In swing time ♩ = 130

Here comes Sal - ly walk - ing down the al - ley, here comes Sal - ly just like that. _

Here comes an - oth - er one just like the oth - er one, here comes an - oth - er one just like that. _ Well I

look down the al - ley and what do I see? A big fat man from Ten - nes - see. _ Well I

bet you five dol - lars I can whoop that man! I bet you five dol - lars I can whoop that man! Well I

jumped to the right, I jumped to the left, I jumped to the right and shim - mied my best!

Singing Sherlock wants to know:

🔍 Are you listening carefully and matching your voice to the leader?

🔍 Are you making sure your actions are not getting in the way of your singing?

🔍 Are your actions in time with your singing?

🔍 Can you use a 'big fat voice' for the man from Tennessee?

SHERLOCK'S CASE NOTES

A fun singing game …

- Stand the children facing each other in two lines, spaced apart to form an 'alley':

- 'Here comes Sally …'
Child A moves down the alley doing a silly walk/creeping/hopping etc.

- 'Here comes another …'
Child B, from the opposite line, moves down the alley copying Child A's silly walk.

- 'Well I looked down the alley …'
ALL peer down the alley, with hand shading eyes

- 'A big fat man from Tennessee …'

- **ALL** indicate a large tummy with both hands.

- 'Well I bet you five dollars I could whoop that man …'
ALL raise one knee slightly and slap with hand on 'whoop'.

- 'Well I jumped to the right …'
ALL move together as suggested by the words.

- As the song progresses, and more children go down the alley, move the lines up to create enough space.

- You could also have two 'Sallys' going down the alley.

Sing a Little Song

performance – CD 1 track 7; backing – CD 1 track 8
starting note – D; introduction – 8 beats

S Wilding

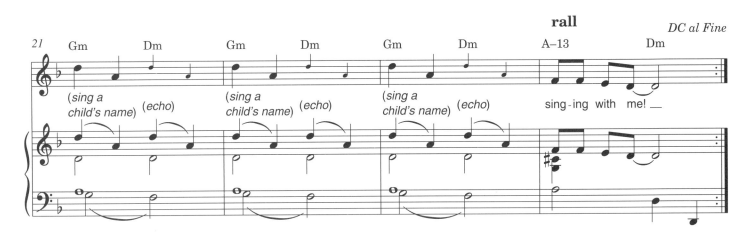

Singing Sherlock wants to know:

- Are you listening carefully so you can match your pitch to the leader?

- On which word does the tune change in the second 'afternoon' section of the song?

- Are you remembering to sound the 't' at the end of words like "light" and "all right" etc.

- Are you making sure your lips are taking a walk away from your teeth to make an 'oo' sound?

SHERLOCK'S CASE NOTES

- The narrow pitch range of this song is useful for helping children to find their singing voice, as well as learning to match their pitch to that of the leader. Other songs, activities and background essentials for developing these skills can be found in *Singing Sherlock Book 2*.

- The song works particularly well if performed with the children sitting in a circle.

- Choose a child whose name you are going to sing. Sing the song, or play the CD, and ask the children to sing the name as an 'echo'.

- Teach the children the whole song, and then divide the group in half. One group sings the melody, and the other group sings the echo.

- Swap over, so each group gets a turn.

- Next invite individuals to perform the echo. If a child is shy, they could sing with a friend.

Hoi Maché Peter

performance – CD 1 track 9; backing – CD 1 track 10
starting note – D; introduction – 8 beats

Traditional

Count in:

1   2   3   4

Hoi ma-ché Pe-ter, Hoi ma-ché Pah.   Hoi ma-ché Pe-ter, Hoi ma-ché Pah.

Hoi ma-ché Pe-ter, Hoi ma-ché Pah.   Hoi ma-ché Pe-ter, Hoi ma-ché Pah.

Singing Sherlock wants to know:

🔍 *Are you listening really carefully and matching your voices to the leader?*

🔍 *Are you sounding the h at the beginning of the word "Hoi"?*

🔍 *Are you using your thinking voice, and hearing the words and notes in your head at the right time?*

🔍 *Are you using your giraffe's neck (see page 9 – Sitting to sing), when you sing the high "Hoi's"?*

SHERLOCK'S CASE NOTES

- *Another song that is really valuable for developing the 'thinking voice'.*

- *Everyone learns the song as written.*

- *On the subsequent singing perform the song as follows:*

  1. *Omit the word 'Peter'*
  2. *Omit the word 'Pah'*
  3. *Omit 'Peter' and 'Pah'*
  4. *Omit 'Hoi Maché*

- *Ask the children to march in time as they sing the song.*

Changing Channels

performance – CD 1 track 11; backing – CD 1 track 12
starting note – E♭; introduction – 11 beats

Jon Laird

I turned on the te-le-vi-sion and who did I see? Sing-ing a lit-tle song look-ing right back at me?

Spoken: A ghost *(ghost face and hands)* Oo oo oo oo Oo oo oo
A princess in a tower *(stroking her hair)* Oh, oh, oh, oh, Oh, oh, oh,
A baby crying! *(head back, eyes closed)* Wah, wah, wah, wah! Wah, wah, wah,
An evil witch *(casting a spell)* Nyah, nyah, nyah, nyah! Nyah, nyah, nyah,
A teacher *(wagging finger)* Sh - hh - hh - h! Sh - hh - hh,
A detective *(stroking his chin)* Hmm - mm - mm - mm. Hmm - mm - mm,
A sheep *(with a wobbly sheep voice)* Baa, baa, baa, baa. Baa, baa, baa,
An opera singer *(with wavy opera hands)* La, la, la, la. La, la, la,

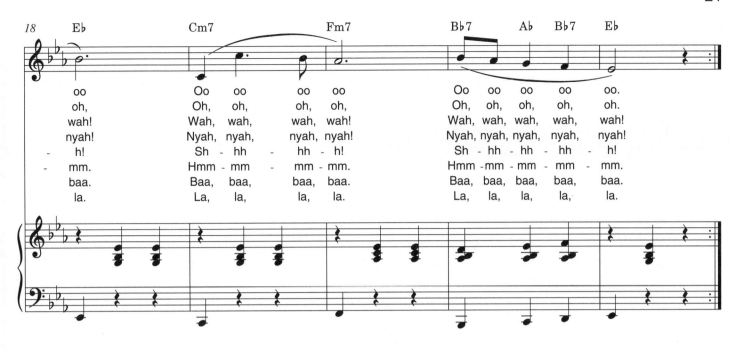

Singing Sherlock wants to know:

- Can you add movements to your singing to depict the characters in each verse?

- Are you using your acting face?

- What kind of vocal quality do you need for the different verses? Have you had a turn at demonstrating a particular vocal quality?

- Are you remembering to make the words "I turned on the television" sound interesting every time you sing them?

- Can you make up verses of your own?

SHERLOCK'S CASE NOTES

- This is a great song for stretching the voice, exploring vocal qualities (see page 11 – Voice Stretch) and acting different characters.

- You do not need to perform all the verses every time you sing the song.

- If a child is not yet able to sing in their head voice/tilt, they may find some of the voice qualities more difficult to perform than others, eg the baby or the sheep.

All Warmed-up

performance – CD 1 track 13; backing – CD 1 track 14
no starting note (vocals rapped); introduction – 8 beats

Kay Umansky

Chorus
Gotta energise the body,
Gotta get the body ready,
Gotta feel that beat,
And we gotta keep it steady.
We're in the mood,
We're in the know,
Get ready, get set,
And here we go!

Verse 1
Gonna pump those lungs,
(Ss, ss, ss, ss, ss, ss)
Gonna dive in the lake,
(Wheeeeeeee – voice slide)
Gonna work those tongues,
(Stick tongues in and out)
Gonna shiver and shake,
(Brrrrrrrrrrrrrrrrrrrrrrrrrrr!).

Then we strike a pose,
And make a stand,
And we punch the air,
With a bold right hand!
(Punch air 8 times)

Chorus
Gotta energise the body,
Gotta get the body ready,
Gotta feel that beat,
And we gotta keep it steady.
We're in the mood,
We're in the know,
Get ready, get set,
And here we go!

Verse 2
Gonna laugh in our boots,
(Ho! Ho, ho, ho, ho, ho!)
Do a firework show,
(VvvVVVVVVVvvvv!)
Make a face like fruits,
*(BIG pumpkin,
tiny little raisin face!)*
Let our lasso go,
(Yeee-hiiiiiii – Yo!).

Then we strike a pose,
And make a stand,
And we punch the air,
With a bold left hand!
(Punch air 8 times)

Chorus
Gotta energise the body,
Gotta get the body ready,
Gotta feel that beat,
And we gotta keep it steady.
We're in the mood,
We're in the know,
Get ready, get set,
And here we go!

Verse 3
Gonna open our throat,
(Ahhhhhhhhhhhhh!)
Gonna talk real posh,
*(Gracious! Do ai really?
Eow mai gosh!)*
Gonna shake, shake, shake,
(shake body vigorously)
Like a dog in the wash,
(Grrrrr --- woof!).

Then we take of the hand,
Of the nearest friend,
And we take a bow,
'Cos we've reached the end!

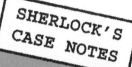

Singing Sherlock wants to know:

- Can you keep a steady pulse by clicking your fingers and stepping throughout the chorus?

- Are you copying the leader accurately with both your voice and your actions?

- Have you had a turn at being the leader and demonstrating the required vocal sound?

- Can you think of some new verses to demonstrate different vocal sounds?

SHERLOCK'S CASE NOTES

- This funky rap includes many of the warm-up activites outlined in Warm-ups (page 8). Start by clicking your fingers and stepping from side to side to the pulse, asking the children to join in.

- Learn the chorus first by call and response – the teacher/leader sings a line and the children sing it back with the appropriate actions.

- Ideas for actions:
  "Gonna energise the body" – open out the arms and chest as if using chest expanders;
  "Feel that beat" – imitate a metronome with your right arm, holding it at the elbow with your left hand;
  "We're in the mood" – thumbs up;
  "In the know" – point to the side of head;
  "Get ready, get set and here we go" – mime a running action with arms.

- You will need to build the verses gradually over a period of time and concentrate on developing the different vocal techniques.

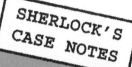

Groovy Grandma

performance – CD 1 track 15; backing – CD 1 track 16
starting note – A♭; introduction – 16 beats

Words traditional
Music by Chris Williams

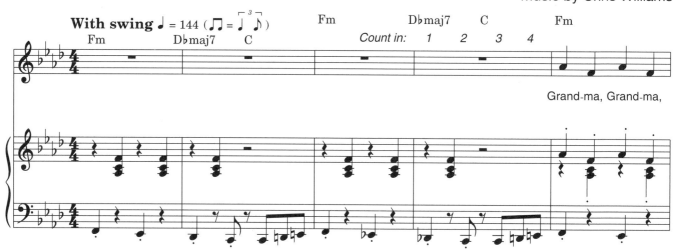

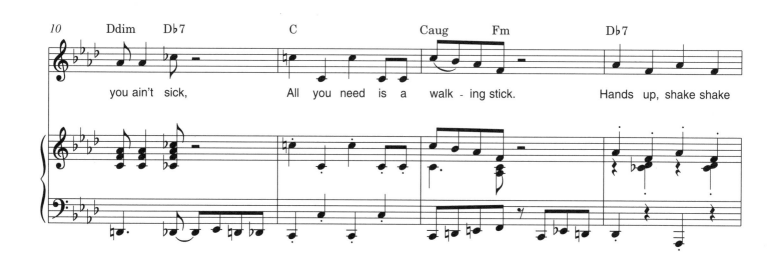

Singing Sherlock wants to know:

- Are you acting the song with your face?

- Are you all performing your actions exactly together?

- Are you using a variety of vocal qualities in your singing?

- Do you remember the repeated sections at the end of the song?

- Can you choose an action to perform on the final "HOT DOG!"?

- Is everyone freezing on this action?

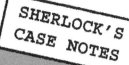

SHERLOCK'S CASE NOTES

- *A song guaranteed to get children singing and moving!*

- Actions:
  "sick in bed"
  – *clutch stomach and look 'poorly'.*
  "She sent for the doctor"
  – *mime a telephone to your ear.*
  "You ain't sick"
  – *point to audience.*
  "All you need is a walking stick"
  – *mime a bent-over old person holding a walking stick with a wobbly hand.*
  "Got the rhythm in my head, ding dong"
  – *tip head from side to side on "ding, dong".*
  "Got the rhythm in the mm, mm"
  – *turn slightly sideways with hands on hips and say "mm, mm" with a cheeky expression.*

- *Take care with the following:*
  octave leaps on "all you need is a",
  "hands down, shake, shake" and
  "bet you five bucks"– bars 11, 19 and 39;
  the accuracy of the notes at bars 20,
  eg the note sung on "got" is the same note as "shake", but in contrast at bar 22 the note sung on "got" goes down.

- *There is a rap version of the first part of this song in Singing Sherlock Book 2.*

Section 2 – Moving On

Clues on unison singing
How to develop a clear vocal tone
and unified sound .. .. *page* 29

Clues on communication and expression
How to communicate a song effectively   30

Songs

Clues on unison singing

How to develop a clear vocal tone and unified sound

Clues	Solutions

Vocal range

Listen! Are the children struggling to sing higher notes in head voice/tilt?
Look! Is the children's posture appropriate?

Make a whining puppy sound (*Voice Stretch* page 11) or do the *Bungee Jumping* warm-up (page 12). Check that the children are standing or sitting tall and not sticking their chins out.

Vowel shapes

Listen! Are the children singing out of tune?
Look! Are they moving their mouths lazily or too much?

Make sure all the children form the same mouth shapes when singing. This will lead to a good, clear vocal tone, better tuning and a blend of the class or group's voices.

Breathing

Listen! Are the children breathing in too quickly and raising their shoulders?
Look! Are they breathing in an inappropriate place during a musical phrase (or sentence), causing the lyrics to lose sense?

Ask the children to imagine their tummy is a big hot-air balloon and they are filling their air tank from the bottom. To retain the sense of the lyrics ask the children to sing through a musical phrase breathing together at the same time.

Lips and tongue (diction)

Listen! Are the words unclear?
Look! Are the children making too much or too little mouth movement?

Make sure that the children's lips and tongues are working well, and that all consonants are sounding together. Try the following steps: whisper the words with an exaggerated mouth; sing the words in a silly voice; sing fast phrases slowly until they can be performed at the required speed. Tongue twisters like *Toboggan* (page 15), are also valuable – and children often like to contribute their own to singing sessions.

Vocal blend

Listen! Can you hear individual voices sticking out? Out-of-tune singing?
An 'over-sung' and forced sound?
Or breathy singing?

Mix children with stronger voices in with those who have weaker voices. Experiment with different groupings to achieve a blended sound. (Too many strong voices placed altogether may result in a competition to see whose voice is loudest.) This type of grouping will also help when singing songs in parts.

Legato singing
(Legato means to play or sing smoothly)

Listen! Are the words over-syllabic (sounding like a robot) or the musical phrases sounding choppy?

Try singing a long vocal phrase to "loo". As you sing trace rainbow shapes in the air with your arms, or mime sewing with a very long needle and thread. Now try the same thing singing the phrase to the correct words.

Clues on communication and expression

How to convey a song effectively to an audience

Clues	Solutions
Focus and silence	There should be a moment of silence before the song begins and after it ends. The children should focus on an imaginary spot in the middle of their teacher's or conductor's face, or an agreed focal point at the back of the room if there is no-one standing in front. Remember, no wandering eyeballs. Also, at the end of the song add a 'freeze moment' or a 'photo shot' so the mood is not broken.
Storytelling	Singing is just the same as acting, but the words are set to music. The audience need to understand and feel what is being communicated to them. Discuss with the children the different moods that need to be captured within a song. Ask them to use their 'acting faces'. Practise looking angry, surprised, excited, confused, sad etc, either to different focus points in the room or to a partner. Children can find it hard to look at one another, so do a lot of practice in pairs mirroring one another's expressions and singing as they face each other. Use different children as 'Sherlock TV detectors' to check that all the other children's 'acting faces' are switched on.
Dynamics *(singing loudly and softly)*	Think about the dynamic contrast needed in the song to match the mood of the lyrics and music. How loudly or softly you sing depends on the amount and speed of the airflow used to make the sounds. Imagine singing with a lighted candle in front of your mouth. Sing a soft "ooh" sound without blowing out your candle. Now sing a louder "ooh" sound, this time blowing out your imaginary candle. Ask the children to imagine their voices have a volume control switch like a CD player or a radio, and use this switch to 'turn' their voices up or down in volume.
Movement and actions	Make sure that all actions are appropriate and add to the performance rather than visually detracting from the singing. It is also important that the children's movements do not hinder the quality of their singing.
Performance goals	In each singing session try and have a 'performance moment', *ie* a complete run through of the song as you have so far learnt it. This allows a sense of achievement for the singers, as well as an opportunity for you – and the children – to assess where they have got to in their performance, and set goals for the next session.
Presentation	Experiment with different ways of grouping children on the stage or performance area. Standing children in rows might be appropriate for many songs, but for a music-theatre-style song it can be effective if the children stand in different spaces, perhaps in a staggered formation or facing sideways etc.

Listen to the River

performance – CD 1 track 17; backing – CD 1 track 18
starting note – A; introduction – 8 beats

Sue Furlong

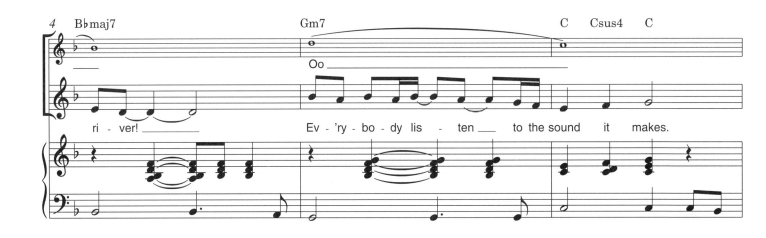

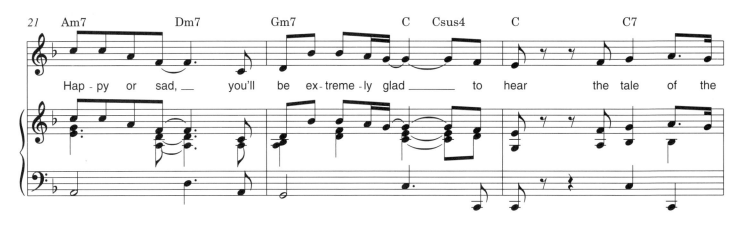

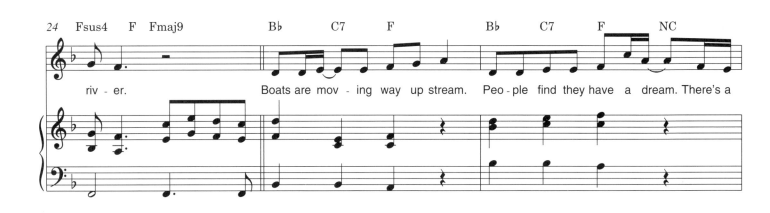

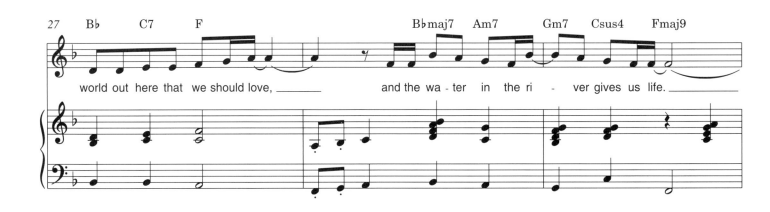

Singing Sherlock wants to know:

- *Can you give the word 'listen' a special emphasis so that the audience really do listen to your tale?*

- *Are you thinking ahead and remembering to repeat the chorus at the end? Can you think of a different way of singing the repeated chorus, eg louder or softer?*

- *Do you remember the difference between the words in verse 1: "there's a world out here that I could love",*
  and verse 2: "there's a world out here that we should love"?

- *If you are singing the 2nd part, are you putting your lips forward to make a good 'oo' shape? Can you make this line really smooth?*

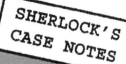

SHERLOCK'S CASE NOTES

- *This has a catchy tune that children will quickly latch onto.*

- *Although the words "Everybody listen" at bar 3 and bar 5 are exactly the same, the rhythm is different. Make sure you teach these accurately.*

- *Enjoy the key change at bar 33, but do not let the children push their voices. Keep the throat open (see Silent Laugh page 10), and the jaw relaxed.*

- *The optional second (harmony) part could be sung by a smaller group of older children. Do not let it overpower the main melody.*

Tramps' Paradise

performance – CD 1 track 19; backing – CD 1 track 20
starting note – G; introduction – 16 beats

Alice Higgins and Martha Wiltshire, aged 11 years

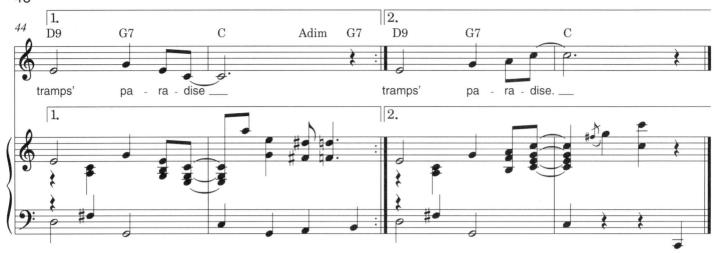

tramps' pa - ra - dise ___   tramps' pa - ra - dise. ___

Singing Sherlock wants to know:

What kind of character is your tramp?

Do your facial expressions and actions help to describe him?

Are you listening really carefully so your voices do not slide over the chromatic notes (notes very close together), eg the word "paradise"?

In the chorus does everyone manage to keep together and sway in the same direction at the same time?

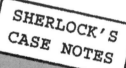

SHERLOCK'S CASE NOTES

- *The composers, Alice and Martha, wrote this song when they were 11 years old!*

- *Talk to the children about tramps, and what their life is really like. Explain that this is an amusing and entertaining song with an image more of a 'cartoon' caricature tramp. It needs to be sung with lots of drama and facial expressions to bring out the humour.*

- *Be careful with small intervals between notes (chromatic notes), eg the opening phrase "tramps paradise" and similarly "now it's just a dump" and "carpets under our feet".*

- *The chorus needs to be sung with a lilt; try swaying to the beat, whilst sticking your thumbs in the lapels of your imaginary tramp's coat.*

- *To add variety, small groups of soloists could sing the verses.*

- *Actions will add to the performance of the song – the children could make up their own.*

A Hero Called Me

performance – CD 1 track 21; backing – CD 1 track 22
starting note – C; introduction – 16 beats

Sue Furlong

Do you want to be a he - ro, do-ing all the things that he - roes do? _

Yes I do. I'll be a he - ro, try to be the ve - ry best for you. _

Are you Ro - bin Hood al-ways do - ing good? No Sir, _
Have you met a king or a prince or two? No Sir, _

things that we do __ are rea - lly from our heart. __ So here we go to be a

he - ro. __ I'm a he - ro called ME!

Singing Sherlock wants to know:

- Are you able to show in your face whether you are the one asking or answering the questions?

- Can you look very proud when you sing the words "I'm a hero called ME"?

- Are you able to use your voice and your body to both sound and look like a King, Prince or a Musketeer?

SHERLOCK'S CASE NOTES

- *This is an echo song in the form of a conversation.*

- *Teach the song as a call and response. The leader sings the 'call': "Do you want to be a hero?" and the children to sing back: "Yes I do, I'll be a hero" etc.*

- *Split the children into two groups; one group sings the 'call', the other sings the response.*

- *Invite small groups and/or soloists to sing either the call or the response.*

- *Choose different postures to represent the different named heroes in the song, eg Robin Hood, Prince and Musketeer.*

- *Select a group of singers to stay on the upper note at the end of the piece to give a very simple but effective two-part ending.*

The Wreck of the Amphitrite

performance – CD 1 track 23; backing – CD 1 track 24
starting note – A; introduction – 15 beats

Chris Williams

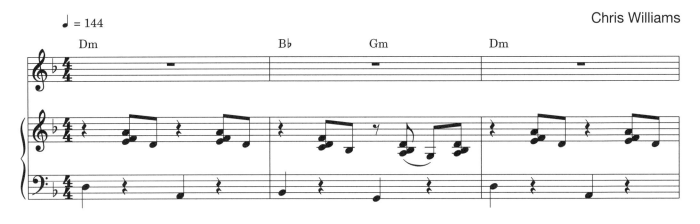

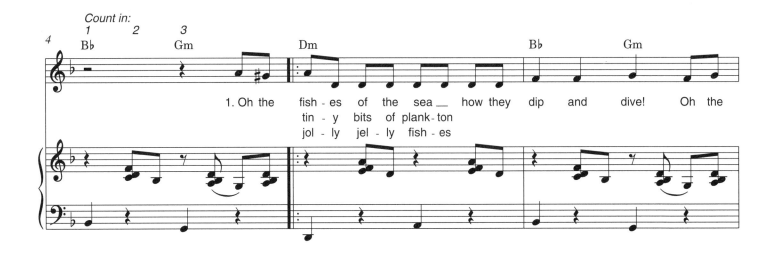

1. Oh the fish-es of the sea __ how they dip and dive! Oh the
tin - y bits of plank-ton
jol - ly jel - ly fish - es

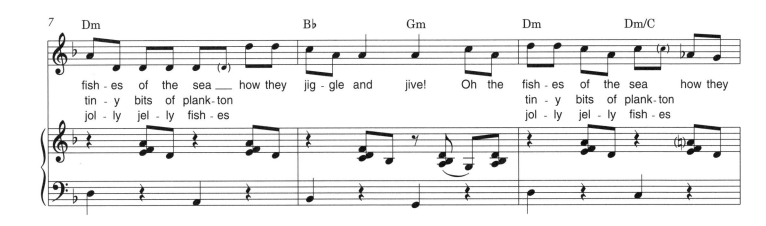

fish - es of the sea __ how they jig - gle and jive! Oh the fish - es of the sea how they
tin - y bits of plank-ton   tin - y bits of plank-ton
jol - ly jel - ly fish - es   jol - ly jel - ly fish - es

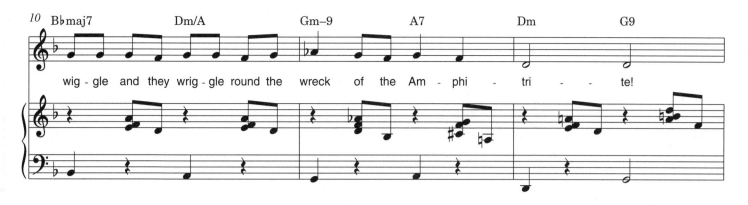

wig - gle and they wrig - gle round the wreck of the Am - phi - tri - - te!

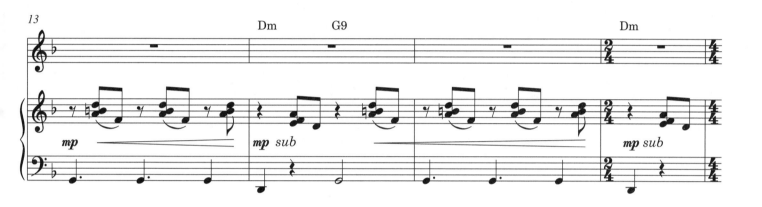

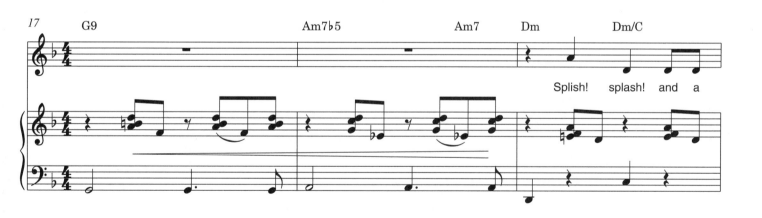

Splish! splash! and a

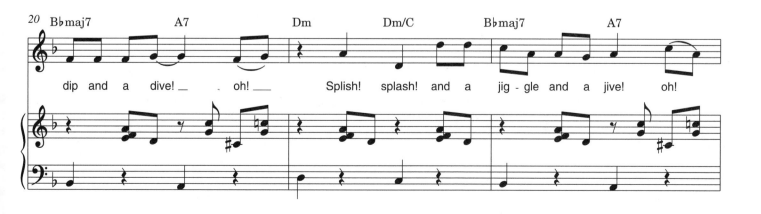

dip and a dive! __ oh! __ Splish! splash! and a jig - gle and a jive! oh!

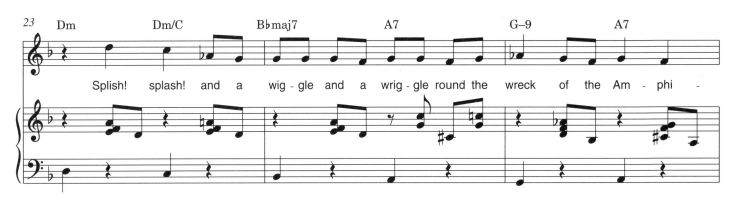

Splish! splash! and a wig - gle and a wrig - gle round the wreck of the Am - phi -

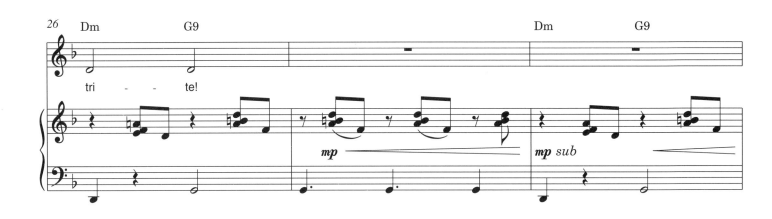

tri - te!

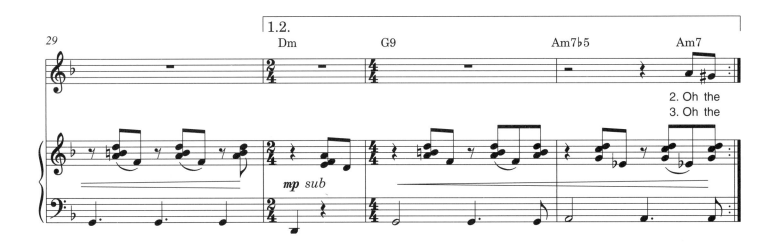

1.2.

2. Oh the
3. Oh the

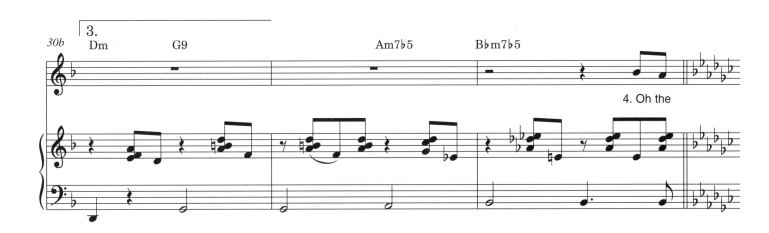

3.

4. Oh the

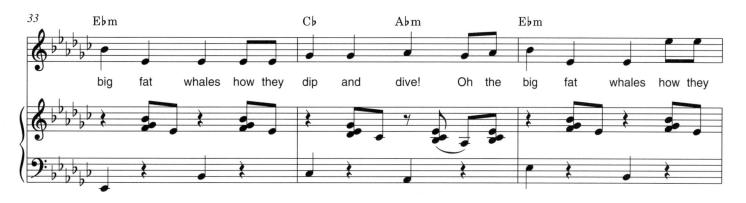

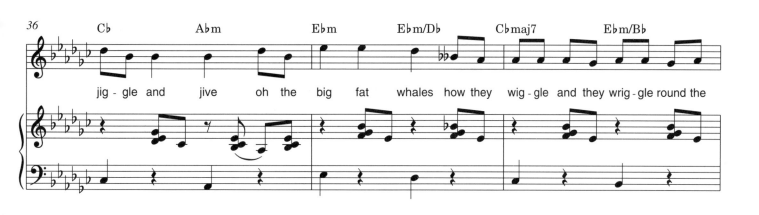

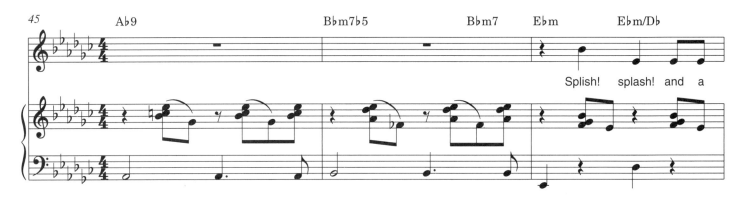

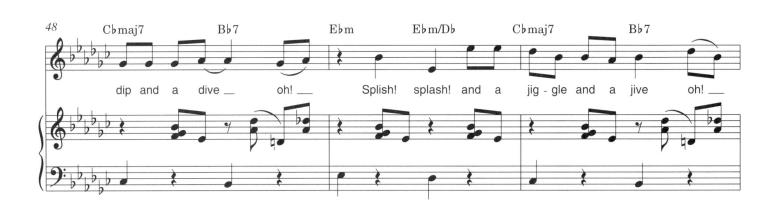

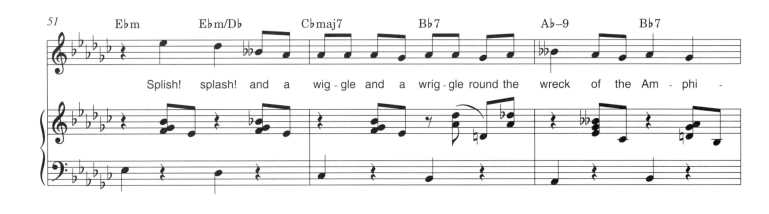

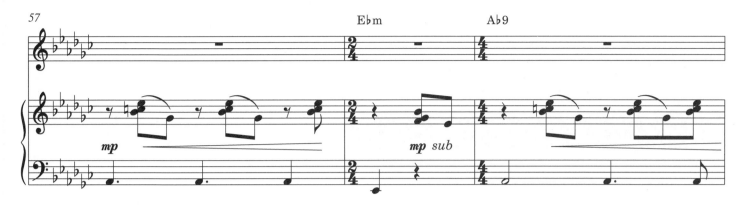

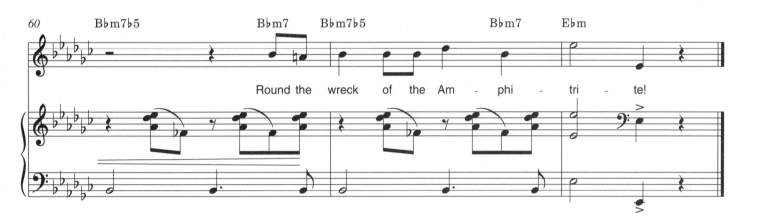

Round the wreck of the Am - phi - tri - te!

Singing Sherlock wants to know:

- *Are you using your tongue and lips to sing words clearly, eg "tiny bits of plankton" and "jolly jellyfish"?*

- *Are you making contrasts using dynamics (loud and soft singing) in the different verses?*

- *Are you making sure you do not get "jiggles", "wiggles" and "wriggles" mixed up?*

SHERLOCK'S CASE NOTES

- *The Amphitrite was a British Convict ship, named after the Greek Goddess Amphitrite. In 1833, the ship was sailing to New South Wales and was wrecked off the coast of Boulogne. 108 female convicts, 12 children and 13 seamen were all drowned.*

- *Explain to the children the song is not about the sad story of the people who drowned, but the various marine life that now enjoy dipping and diving around the wreck.*

- *Start by teaching the chorus.*

- *The following are actions that we have used (but you can make up your own.)*
  To ensure children feel the rests at bars 19, 21 and 23 try making a body sound or a movement, eg clap, then let the hands explode outwards for the "splish splash", then bring them together again, making them dive forward on "dip and a dive". Clap again, but then do a little body jig on "jiggle and jive". Clap once more, and do 'roly-poly' hand actions on "wiggle and a wriggle".

- *Make sure all the pick-up notes before the words "fishes of the sea" are sung accurately.*

- *Make sure the children are really familiar with the rests between each verse and chorus.*

- *To stop the children sliding on the final octave leap "tri-te", ask the children to sing these as short, separated notes before singing as written.*

Sporting World

performance – CD 1 track 25; backing – CD 1 track 26
starting note – G; introduction – 2 beats before claps

Alison Carver

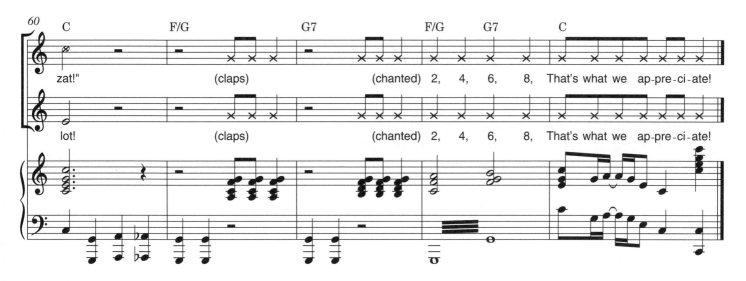

Singing Sherlock wants to know:

- *Are all your words still clear when you sing in parts?*

- *Are you all clapping exactly together and in time?*

- *Are you able to perform your actions without it interfering with your singing?*

- *When singing in parts are you making sure that your line is not overpowering the other line?*

- *Are you taking care not to get too excited and shout rather than sing, particularly in the football verse?*

SHERLOCK'S CASE NOTES

- *Even if the children get excited when singing about their favourite sport, you must always aim for pitch accuracy and a clear vocal tone.*

- *Ask the children to make up different sporting actions for each verse. Make sure that the actions chosen do not detract from the singing.*

- *You may like to begin by dividing the class into four groups, with each group representing a different sport. Ask each group to hold a pose that depicts their sport until it is their turn to sing, rather like a photograph.*

- *When it is their turn to sing each group 'comes alive'. After they have sung they resume their 'photo frame picture' again.*

- *In the tennis verse, to help the children feel the rests, give them a movement to perform before the words "throw the ball" and "serve and run".*

Singing the Greens

performance – CD 1 track 27; backing – CD 1 track 28
starting note – D; introduction – 8 beats

Kay Umansky

You're sing-ing the blues, I'm sing-ing the
greens, you're sing-ing the

greens, I'm sing-ing of sprouts in vast a-mounts, I'm sing-ing of beans. I'm sing-ing of
blues, I'm sing-ing of all the foods I choose to stick in my stews, I'm sing-ing of

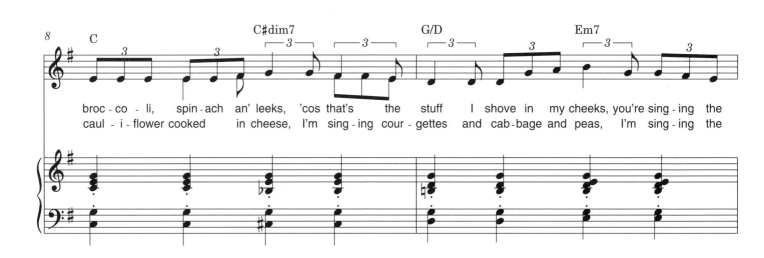

broc-co-li, spin-ach an' leeks, 'cos that's the stuff I shove in my cheeks, you're sing-ing the
caul-i-flower cooked in cheese, I'm sing-ing cour-gettes and cab-bage and peas, I'm sing-ing the

56

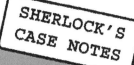

SHERLOCK'S CASE NOTES

- *This song needs very clear and articulated words. (See Tongue Workout on page 10).*

- *Because the song is very wordy, teach only small sections at a time. Simple actions will help the children remember the words and will add a dramatic element to the song.*

- *Beware of the very small intervals between the notes (chromatic notes). The children will need to listen very carefully to make sure that these are accurate.*

- *The children will need lots of energy and breath support to manage the ascending phrase on "Everything I need" and at the end of the song on "Singing the Greens" where the melody goes up.*

Singing Sherlock wants to know:

- *Are you singing as if you are having a conversation with someone? Can you express the different of opinions of the two people in the song?*

- *Are you using the tip of your tongue and your lips to make the words crystal clear?*

- *Can you make different gestures to illustrate all the opposites in the song, eg 'sun' and 'rain', 'grass' and 'grease'.*

- *Are you making the audience laugh?*

Shoes

performance – CD 1 track 29; backing – CD 1 track 30
starting note – E; introduction – 6 beats

Lin Marsh

3rd time through jump to 3rd time bar on page 61

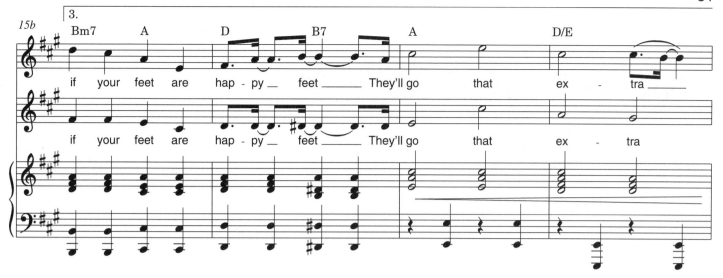

Singing Sherlock wants to know:

🔍 *Are you keeping your long giraffe's neck (see* Sitting to Sing, *page 9) and dropping your jaw when you sing "go that extra mile", "in a trice" and "grand plié"?*

🔍 *Are you making all the consonants (beginnings and ends of words) really clear?*

🔍 *What is the mood of this song? Are you communicating this with your facial expression?*

SHERLOCK'S CASE NOTES

■ *There are a lot of words in this song, so teach it in small sections and build it up over a period of time.*

■ *Adding actions will really enhance this song, as well as help the children remember the words. Children are usually experts at making up actions, so use their ideas.*

■ *Part 2 lies quite high in the voice, and it may be preferable to teach this part to older, or more experienced children. Take care with the octave leap from bar 5 to 6 "shoes to have some fun in". Make sure the children do not strain their necks or poke their chins forward, but keep a floppy jaw and relaxed tongue.*

■ *Help the children to access the higher notes of this song by using some vocal warm-up exercises, eg Bungee Jumping (page 12).*

Feel the Groove

performance – CD 1 track 31; backing – CD 1 track 32
starting note – F; introduction – 13 beats

Jon Laird

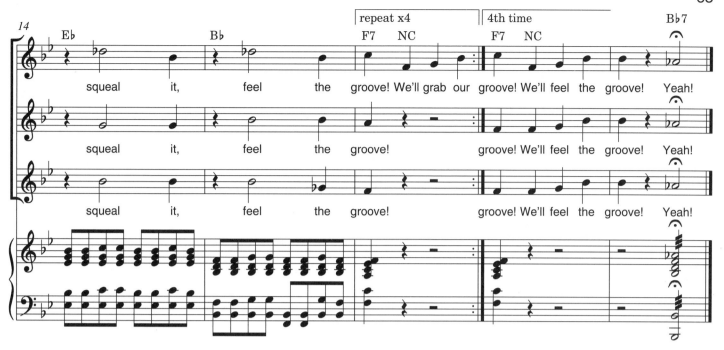

Singing Sherlock wants to know:

- Can you make up an action for each line of the song? Do hand jive actions to one of the parts.

- Have you had a go at being a conductor and leading one of the vocal parts to help keep the singers together?

- When you sing the song for the final time do you remember to sing the correct ending?

- Can you use a twangy sound in your voice to suit the pop style of the song?

SHERLOCK'S CASE NOTES

- *This is an example of a 'layered' song, which works by dividing the class or singers into as many parts as there are vocal lines. Each group repeats their line, adding each subsequent line one by one until all the vocal lines/parts are singing at the same time.*

- *Teach the children to sing part 1 of this song first. Choose an appropriate action for the words and song, eg mime singing with a microphone.*

- *Teach them part 2. Only when both parts are secure separately should you try them together.*

- *Use the same approach to part 3.*

- *In a concert you might like to invite the audience to join in singing one of the parts.*

- *The children may have difficulty pitching the starting note of the 2nd part. Help them by asking them to sing the first three notes of the 1st voice part in their heads, ie "We'll grab our", and then ask them to pause on the "Ooh" of the 2nd part.*

Section 3 – Clued In

Clues to vocal harmony .. .. *page* 66

Songs

Clues to vocal harmony

Clues	Solutions

Unison is the key

Part-singing can be one of the most exciting experiences for young singers and once they have got the bug they will never look back. However, it is better to sing a unison song really well than to attempt a song in parts that the children can barely manage. Make sure the children can sing confidently in unison, with a clear vocal tone and with expression before introducing parts. In this book all the songs with vocal harmonies can be sung just as effectively in unison.

Lay the foundations

Echo songs (*Sing A Little Song* page 17, *A Hero Called Me* page 41), rounds (*Toboggan* page 15, *Young Rider* page 78), and layered songs (*Feel the Groove* page 62), provide good foundations for more extended part-songs.

The more the merrier!

Singing in larger groups makes part-singing more attainable, as there is safety in numbers. The smaller the group, the more vocally secure your singers need to be.

Feel the pulse

Everyone must be able to feel an internal pulse while singing, otherwise there is a tendency to get faster or for the parts to get out of synch.

Listen carefully

Encourage each group always to listen to themselves and to each other. The idea is not to compete with the other group, but to work as a team, making a beautiful sound when the lines are sung together.

Balance the parts

Make sure you place those children with stronger voices and sharper ears in both parts. Sit children with weaker ears between two stronger singers.

Keep it simple

If the parts in the song are complicated, then look for an easier option first. Find places where the parts echo one another (*eg Hats* page 90) or where the melody is shared between two parts (*In the End* page 146). Quality and accuracy is more important than trying to sing too many parts too soon. It is easier to sing songs with independent parts that fit together. *Night Riders* (page 103) for example, has two distinct melodies that fit together. The children learn both parts and take turns to sing each one. Songs with parts that move in similar motion a 3rd apart (*eg Amani Utupe,* page 71) are more difficult for inexperienced singers, who tend to drift onto the other part.

Share the parts out

For more substantial part-songs, teach the 2nd part to a different group of children at another time. Then bring both groups together to sing the song in two parts.

Spuds

performance – CD 1 track 33; backing – CD 1 track 34
starting note – D; introduction – 24 beats

Chris Hazell

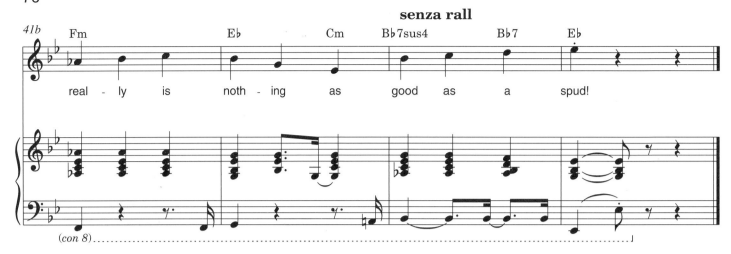

senza rall

real - ly is noth - ing as good as a spud!

(con 8)

Singing Sherlock wants to know:

🔍 *Can you make up some actions that will capture the mood of this song?*

🔍 *Are you managing to sing with your tongue in the side of your mouth to create the effect of singing with a mouthful of 'spuds'? Can the audience still understand what you are singing?*

🔍 *Are you remembering to think ahead to the last chorus where the words change? Do not forget the different ending!*

🔍 *Are you singing this song as if spuds really are your favourite dish?*

SHERLOCK'S CASE NOTES

- Spuds *is one of the songs from a larger children's choral work called* The Journey. *Three other songs from this piece are also included in the 'Sherlock in Concert' section (page 106).*

- *Danger spot: remember that the opening introduction is repeated again before singing verse 3.*

- *Verse 2 should be sung with the tongue (literally) in cheek, as though with a mouthful of food – well, potato!*

- *The song benefits from actions to bring out the humour.*

- *Remember not to slow down at the end on the words "There really is nothing as good as a spud".*

Amani Utupe

performance – CD 2 track 1; backing – CD 2 track 2
starting note – C; introduction – 16 beats

Patsy Ford Simms

With free rhythmic expression, don't rush ♩ = *c*116–120

Singing Sherlock wants to know:

- Are you sounding the k's exactly together on the words "fork" and "talk"?

- Are you making the correct mouth shape with your lips forward on the "lu" of "Hallelujah"?

- Can you use your voice to build the excitement as each new verse starts on a new note (because the music has changed key)?

- Can you use your 'volume control switch' (see page 31) when you sing the final "Grant us peace, give us courage" and sing very softly? Do not forget the long notes on "Amani utupe na ustawi".

- Can you gradually increase the volume towards the end of the song?

- *The words "Amani utupe" mean "Grant us peace, give us courage".*

- *Start by teaching the phrase "Amani utupe na ustawi" then sing the song (or play the CD) asking the children to join in with the phrase everytime it comes throughout the verse and chorus.*

- *Teach them the following actions: on the word "Amani" put your right hand out with palm facing upwards. Similarly, on "utupe na u-" put your left hand out, palm upwards. On "-sta-" put your right hand on the left side of your chest (and leave it there), then put your left hand on the right side of your chest on "-wi", making a cross shape.*

- *In the chorus you may like to sway and clap 'off the beat'.*

- *When you sing the long notes at the end of the song using the syllables "-stawi" (bar 64), slowly lift up both arms in the air, raising them into a V shape on the last word of the song.*

- *Be aware that there is no pause between the verse and chorus; do not be tempted to make a break – it will not fit with the accompaniment.*

- *Children will find this song easy to learn in unison. It is more demanding to sing in parts.*

Young Rider

performance – CD 2 track 3; backing – CD 2 track 4
starting note – G; introduction – 8 beats

Count in: 1   2   3   4

Traditional

Young ri - der, ap - ple-cheeked one, Oh, whi - ther ri - - ding? On your steed so
Young ri - der, ap - ple-cheeked one, Oh, whi - ther ri - - ding? On your steed so

proud and pran - cing, Oh, whi - ther ri - - ding? No mat - ter where I ride
black and hand-some, Oh, whi - ther ri - - ding? No mat - ter where I roam

Slo - vak moun-tains at my side. Du-scha-mo - ya, Du-scha-mo - - ya.
Slo - vak moun-tains are my home. Du-scha-mo - ya, Du-scha-mo - - ya. Hey!

Singing Sherlock wants to know:

🎵 Are you standing well with open shoulders so that you are feeling strong and confident?

🎵 Are you flicking your tongue on the word "Young", to make a strong and positive start?

🎵 Are you giving the word "riding" enough energy and breath support to make a strong, clear sound?

🎵 Have you had a go at being a conductor and leading one of the vocal parts to help keep the singers together?

SHERLOCK'S CASE NOTES

- *The origin of this song is obscure. Some sources state that it is Slovakian, with the tune dating around 1607. "Duschamoya" means "little sweetheart", or "my love". Another source states it is Serbo-Croatian, and that Duschamoya means "Joy of my soul". It is a very popular campfire or Scout song in America.*

- *Like all rounds, the children need to be able to sing the song well in unison before attempting to sing it in three parts.*

- *The song needs a sense of vitality, so feeling a strong first beat in every bar will help the rhythmic lilt to the piece.*

- *The song is really effective if sung unaccompanied, and will allow the children to hear the interweaving of the vocal lines.*

Chocolate Dreams

performance – CD 2 track 5; backing – CD 2 track 6
starting note – G; introduction – 40 beats

Chris Williams

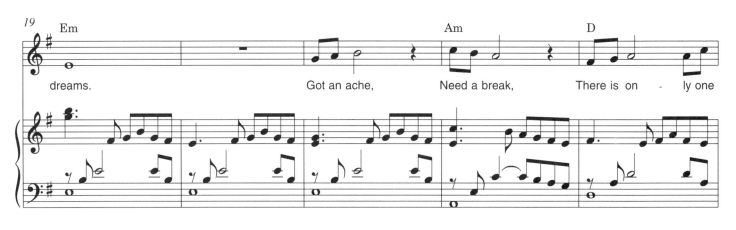

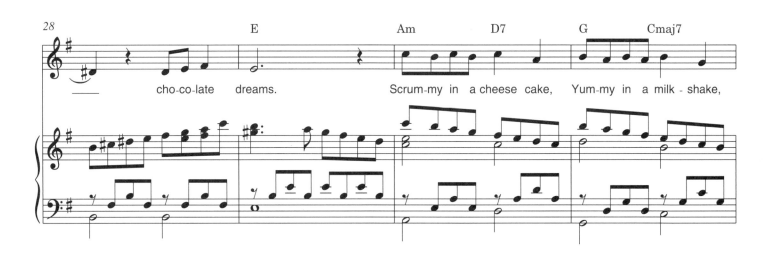

Singing Sherlock wants to know:

🎵 Are you remembering important mouth shapes like "down" and "frown" so that you make a unified "ow" sound with an oval shaped mouth?

🎵 Are you remembering to breathe in a sensible place, and not in the middle of a sentence?

🎵 Are you communicating the words in such a way so that the audience want to rush out and buy some chocolate?

SHERLOCK'S CASE NOTES

- *A song for chocoholics …*

- *Make a slight crescendo (getting louder) through the long note "dream" so that the note does not die away and is lost.*

- *Emphasise the beginning of the word "chocolate" and add an aspirate/whisper quality to give it an added "magic melt-in-the-mouth" sound.*

- *Enjoy the words in the "Scrummy in a cheese cake" section. The consonants need to be especially clear with lots of emphasis on the 'mm' in the middle of the words.*

- *Asking the children to sing to three chosen focus points in the room can help the chocolate goodies in the song come to life, rather than sounding as if they are singing a shopping list.*

- *Beware that the children can easily confuse the melodic line of the words "need a break" (bar 22) with the opening melodic line "feeling blue". This also applies to the 2nd verse on the word "overcome" (bar 53).*

Surf, Surfin' On the Internet

performance – CD 2 track 7; backing – CD 2 track 8
starting note – D; introduction – 31 beats

Music by Ian Blick
Words by Tony Brown

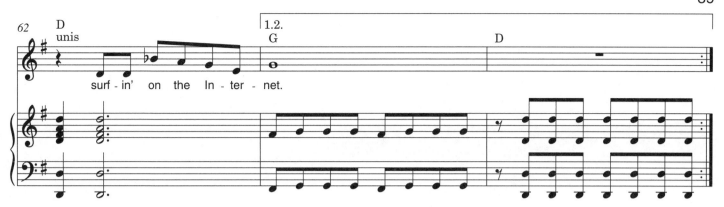

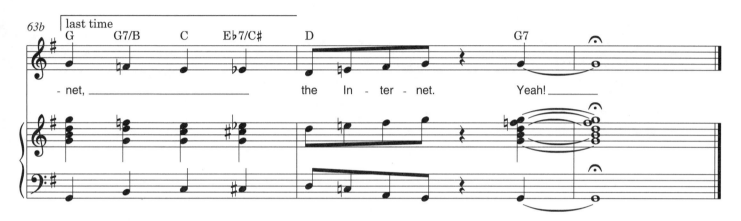

Singing Sherlock wants to know:

🔍 *Are all your words really clear?*

🔍 *Are your lips forward when you sing the "oo" backing vocals? Are you all making the same mouth shape for your "ah" backing vocals? Imagine a 'smile inside your mouth'.*

🔍 *If you are a backing group singer can you make up a surfing dance routine to fit with the song?*

🔍 *Are all your movements at exactly the same time as one another?*

🔍 *There is a long introduction to this song. Can you show with both your face and body that you are fully involved in the song from the very beginning – not just when you start to sing?*

SHERLOCK'S CASE NOTES

■ *This song is a pastiche of the 1960's American rock 'n' roll band called The Beach Boys. They were famous for their close vocal harmonies and lyrics about surfing in California. You might like to play the children one of their famous surfing songs, eg Surfin' USA, or Fun, Fun, Fun.*

■ *Practise this song by first speaking, then singing the words slowly, before performing up to the appropriate tempo (speed).*

■ *Presentation is all-important for this song to have its full impact. Think about where the backing vocalists will stand, eg at either side of the main singing group or all at one side.*

■ *Movements will enhance the mood and the feel of the song.*

■ *For a simple part-singing option, try the top line of backing vocals "Surf, surfin on the internet" (bar 11 and 15).*

Hats

performance – CD 2 track 9; backing – CD 2 track 10
starting note – F; introduction – 16 beats

Hank Beebe

Lightly ♩ = 138

Count in: 1 2 3 4

Hats were made _ for your head,

for when _ it is cold out - side to keep you warm in - stead. _____

simile

_____ Hats can give _ you that

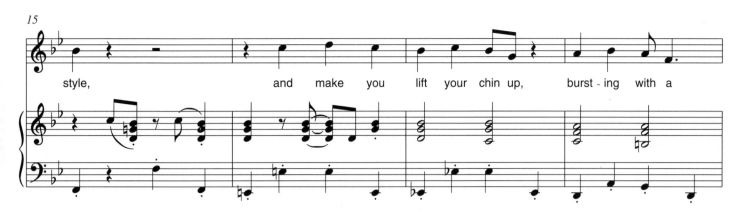

style, and make you lift your chin up, burst-ing with a

smile. _____ But hats can say _ a whole

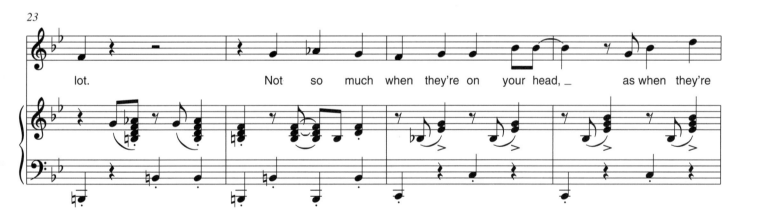

lot. Not so much when they're on your head, _ as when they're

not: _____ Like when _ you say hats off to

sun - ny Sa - tur-days, hats off to choc - 'late an - y - thing, hats off to

friends loy - al and true _____ and that's why

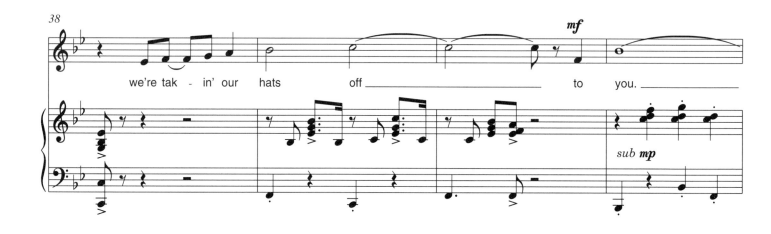

we're tak - in' our hats off _____ to you. _____

77
unis
you.
sub *mf*
f

Singing Sherlock wants to know:

- Can you use a 'twang' in your voice to create the right vocal sound for an American music-theatre-style?

- Are you sustaining your long notes without losing energy, eg "to keep you warm instead"?

- Are you making sure you do not hold on to notes that are followed by rests?

- Are you making sure the final note is only one beat long?

- Are you co-ordinating your hat routine and movements with your singing?

SHERLOCK'S CASE NOTES

- *This song demands the integration of three areas of performance skill: singing the correct notes with the appropriate vocal quality, the communication of the text of each line to make the story come alive, and co-ordination of movements and hats which should enhance, rather than detract from the singing.*

- *For a simple part-singing option, sing just the little echo phrases "the very same hats" and "can cover your hair" (bars 57–60).*

- *Make up some movements using hats to accompany the song as you sing. Teach the song from the outset with mimed hat movements. When notes and movements are secure, practise with your hats.*

- *Plan carefully how to distribute the hats to the children before they perform the song in concert.*

- *Danger spots: on the words "friends loyal and true" (bars 34 –35), if the children are singing in two parts, remind them not to sing the lower part here! This only comes at the end of the song (bar 71). On the final words "to you" (bar 76), notice the notes are different from the beginning.*

A World Without Love

performance – CD 2 track 11; backing – CD 2 track 12
starting note – B; introduction – 16 beats

Sue Furlong

Singing Sherlock wants to know:

- *Can you think of times when you have had an argument with your sister, brother or a friend?*

- *Can you remember how you felt?*

- *Can you practise using your acting face by singing the song to a partner, or different focus points in the room?*

- *Are you singing all your words together in the correct rhythm?*

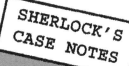

SHERLOCK'S CASE NOTES

- *This is a song with a strong message, so discuss with the children the meaning and implications of the words.*

- *The syncopated rhythms give the song its pop 'feel'. Ensure these are learned accurately, so the vocal line is completely unified, otherwise it will sound messy.*

- *If singing the song in unison only, you could experiment with combinations of small groups and/or soloists singing different sections.*

- *The chorus 'hook' "for a world of war" also includes an echo in the other voice parts. For a simple introduction to part-singing add just the higher part of the echo. The rest of the part-singing is quite challenging, particularly when the lower part sings the sustained lines to "aw" (bar 56–63).*

Night Riders

performance – CD 2 track 13; backing – CD 2 track 14
starting note – D; introduction – 6 beats

Alan Simmons

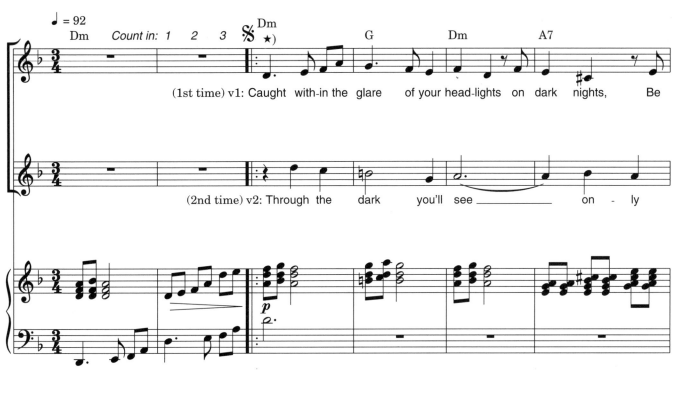

★) On DS sing v1 & v2 together

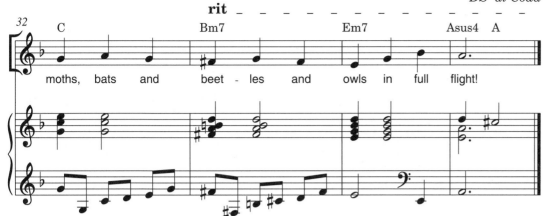

Singing Sherlock wants to know:

🔍 *What is the mood of the song? Can you create the scene and imagine all the creatures coming out after dark?*

🔍 *When singing the second melody "Through the dark you'll see" do you remember to feel all the rests?*

🔍 *Are you taking special care with your consonants to get all t's and k's exactly together?*

🔍 *Can you sing this song very smoothly and with a gentle lilt?*

SHERLOCK'S CASE NOTES

- *Teach this initially as a unison song, with everyone learning both parts.*

- *This song needs to be sung legato (smoothly), with plenty of breath support on the higher notes so that the voices do not sag and go flat.*

- *Before the children sing their entry to the second part, ask them to hear the first note "Through" in their heads with their thinking voice to ensure they pitch accurately.*

- *The song requires a lot of 'word painting' to bring the meaning alive.*

- *Please note that although the parts are distinct, the vocal skills required to sing this song well are quite demanding.*

Sherlock in Concert

Stage Songs and the songs from *The Journey* can be sung either as medleys, or as individual items in a concert – they lend themselves well to movement, actions or simple gestures.

Songs

Songs from *The Journey*

Performance Backing

Songs from *Stage Songs*

The final countdown

" You've learnt the words, you know the song ... "

The performance starts from the moment you walk onto the stage or performance area

- Walk tall and stand proud
- Do not wave at your Mum and Dad
- Be audience-friendly at all times – smile as you walk on stage, between songs, and during the applause

Tell the story

- Switch on your eyes and your acting face
- Stay in character: Who are you? Where are you?
- Feel the emotion of the song, and the audience will feel it too

Be a team player – every singer matters 😊 ✗

The song begins the second before the first note is played.

Hold the silence before and after the song.

And now ...
It's the moment you've been waiting for ...

The Performance!

Motorway Cones

from *The Journey*

Chris Hazell

performance – CD 2 track 15; backing – CD 2 track 16
starting note – B; introduction – 16 beats

Brightly ♩ = *c*144

8 lower throughout

Work - ing on the mo - tor - way, ___ You should hear what peo - ple say ___ a - bout
Just like sol - diers on par - ade, ___ On re - flec - tion we won't fade, ___ we
Wait - ing in a ten mile queue, Bet you're dy - ing for the loo. ___ Oh

me ___ me and my friends. ___
stand ___ all ov - er the land. ___
dear! ___ You won't find one here. ___

Singing Sherlock wants to know:

Who are the different characters in this song? As you sing, imagine you are a cartoon orange motorway cone with a silver stripe across your middle; a self-important policeman; a frustrated driver in a traffic jam.

Are you using your different voice qualities for each character? For example, your 'twangy' voice to make the sound of the "nee-nar" police sirens and a cockney/Eastenders accent for the policeman on "Ow fast do you want to go?"

Are you using your 'volume control switch' (see page 31) to make a decrescendo (getting softer) on the police siren "nee-nars" to give the effect of the police car zooming by?

SHERLOCK'S CASE NOTES

- Be careful the children do not force the vocal sound in their efforts to portray the characters.

- Where there are phrases with repeated notes (eg "working on the", bar 5) make sure that they are not sung mechanically, and give them shape. Acting each character as they sing will help the children achieve this.

- The children will have fun making up appropriate actions to bring out the humour and drama.

- Danger spot: beware the children do not confuse the notes of "me and my friends" (bar 10) with the notes "you're gonna be late" (bar 18). This also applies to the other verses.

- Be careful to observe the length of notes at the end of phrases; notice they are not consistent!

Blackpool

from *The Journey*

performance – CD 2 track 17; backing – CD 2 track 18
starting note – F♯; introduction – 16 beats

Chris Hazell

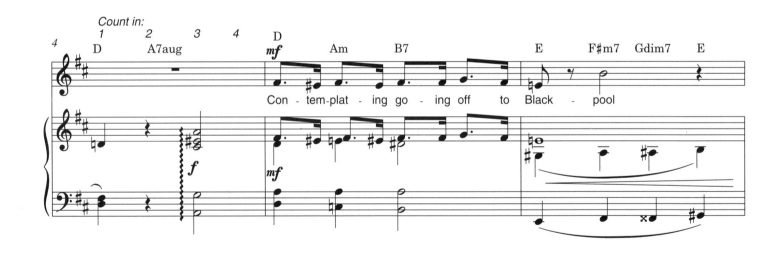

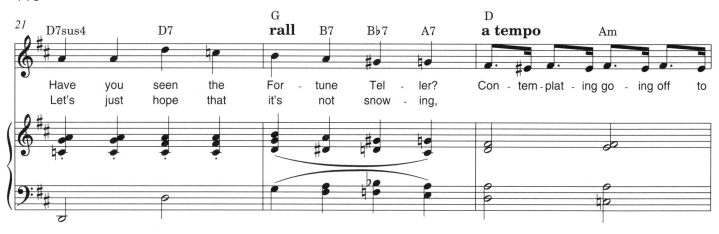

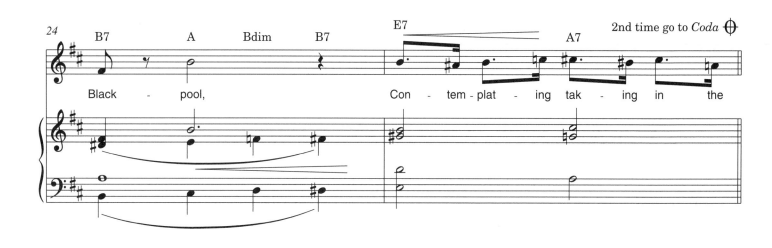

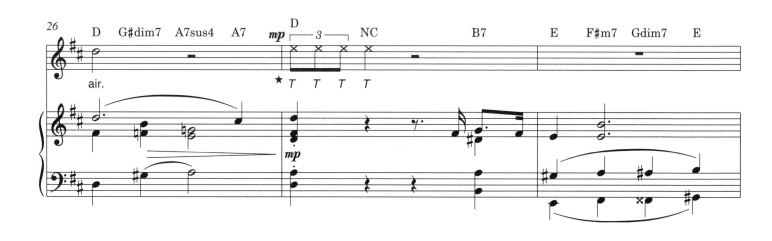

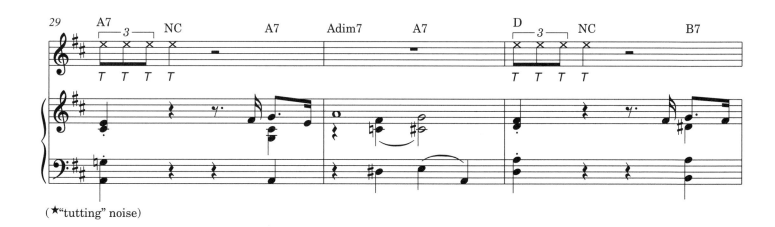

(★"tutting" noise)

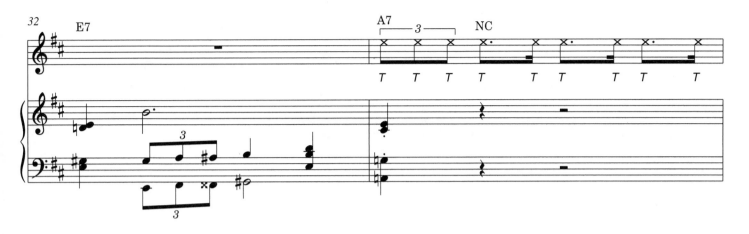

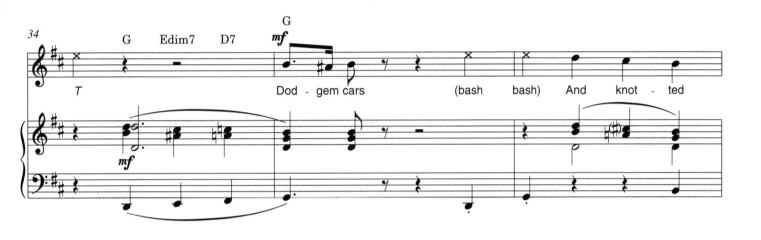

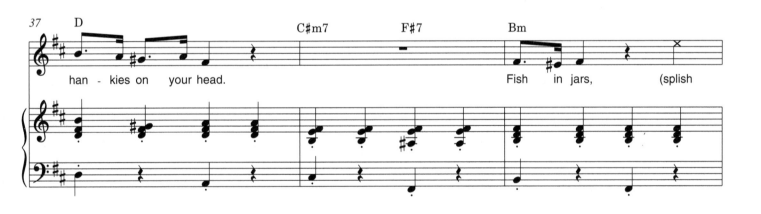

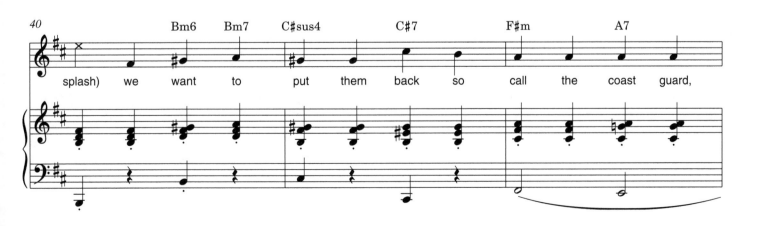

Singing Sherlock wants to know:

🔍 *Can you use different voice qualities to characterise the song? For example, sing with a broad Lancashire accent and sing the word "Blackpool" as "Blackpewl".*

🔍 *Hold your nose on "Mr Punch"; sing "Cor blimey!" like Eastenders; make your "la la la's" very loud and raucous.*

🔍 *The words are very humorous; are you singing in a way that will make the audience laugh?*

🔍 *When tapping your toes and bobbing up and down, are you all starting your movements exactly together, and staying in time throughout?*

🔍 *At the end of the song are you remembering to sing "Cor blimey!" Do not slow down!*

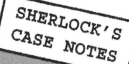

SHERLOCK'S CASE NOTES

■ *This song needs to go with a real swing. Talk to the children about how excited they feel when they are going away on holiday.*

■ *The rallentando (getting slower) at "Fortune Teller" (bar 22), should not begin too early. The children should not to slow down at the beginning of the phrase "Have you seen". The same applies to the next verse.*

■ *Take care with the notes of "Contemplating going off to" (bar 45 and 46). These are not the same as the opening notes of the song, and can be very easily confused.*

■ *At the "T, T, T, T" section (bar 27), add the following tapping movements with your feet as you say the tutting sounds –*
tap your right foot twice as you say:
"T T T T"
(tap)   (tap)
tap your left foot twice as say:
"T T T T"
(tap)   (tap)
tap your right foot twice as you say:
"T T T T"
(tap)   (tap)
tap your left foot five times as you say:
"T T T T   TT   TT   TT
(tap)   (tap) (tap) (tap) (tap)

■ *At the instrumental interlude where the piano plays a spoof version of "Oh We Do Like To Be Beside the Seaside" (bar 49), bob up and down on the beat with thumbs in the air.*

■ *In the "La, la, la" section (bar 56 onwards), make fists and swing both arms vigorously from side to side.*

Where Do We Go from Here?

from *The Journey*

performance – CD 2 track 19; backing – CD 2 track 20
starting note – D; introduction – 32 beats

Chris Hazell

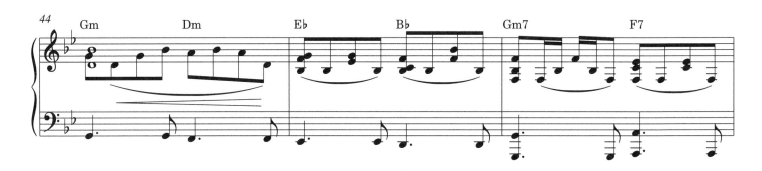

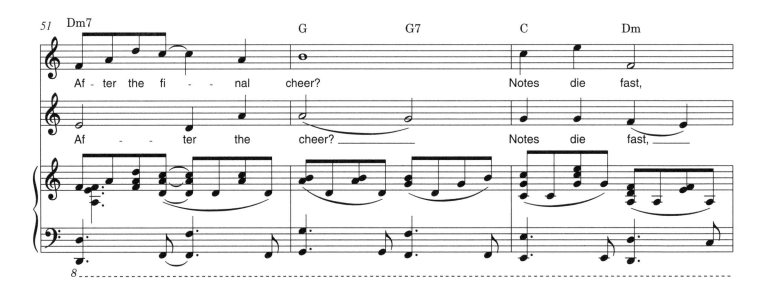

Singing Sherlock wants to know:

🎵 Are you thinking about what the words of the song say, about life being a journey? Our life is a journey – a journey where we can never be sure of our destination and what sort of challenges, successes, highs and lows we will meet on the way.

🎵 Can you practise long phrases in this song by tracing rainbows in the air with your arms as you sing them?

🎵 Can you keep your focus and hold the emotion during the introduction and instrumental section?

🎵 Have you enough breath and energy for the last triumphant note?

SHERLOCK'S CASE NOTES

- This is a fantastic song to end a concert. It has a very emotional core that can touch both singers and audience.

- Build the emotion gradually. Do not begin too loudly; the music needs to incease in intensity towards the key change (bar 49). The music here is marked Maestoso, which means majestic.

- Be careful with the falling notes at "Will **we know** where **to go**" (bar 21 and 22) and make sure the children do not land too heavily on these, but sing them evenly. This also applies to the second verse.

- At "What's in store" (bar 29), ask the children to sing smoothly, keeping the tone flowing right through the long sustained notes.

- The top part "Aah Dreams be want to be" (bars 35–38), will need some attention to ensure the children sing this accurately.

- The piece needs a good strong finish but beware the children do not force or oversing the last note.

Stage Fright

from *Stage Songs*

performance – CD 2 track 21; backing – CD 2 track 22
starting note – D; introduction – 10 beats

Lyrics by Nick Stimson
Music by Chris Williams

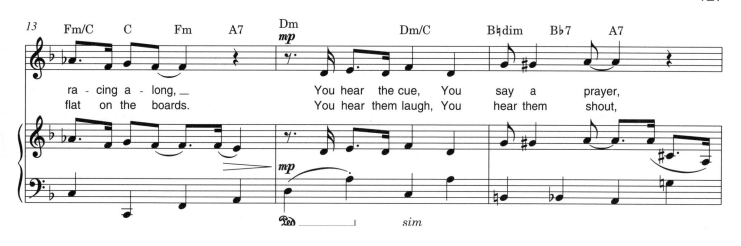

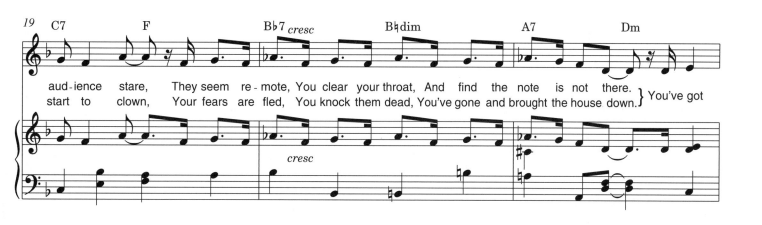

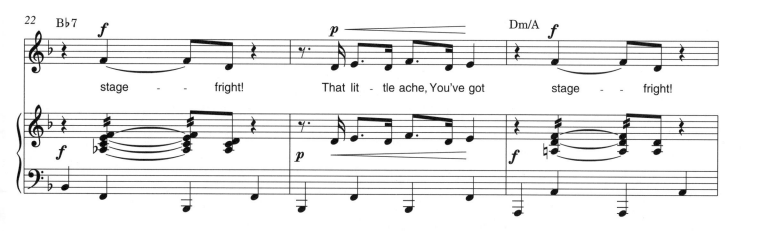

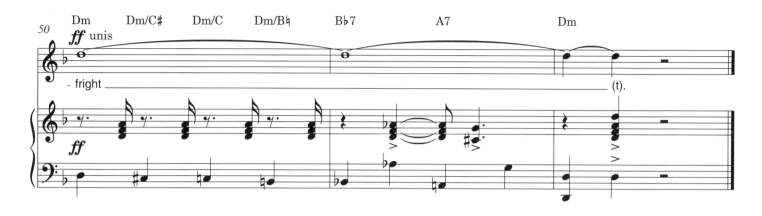

Singing Sherlock wants to know:

What do the words 'stage fright' mean to you?

Have you appointed a 'Sherlock Diction Detective' to check that all ends of words are clear and sung exactly together?

Are you all making the same mouth shape on the words "night after night after night"? Can you imagine a smile inside your mouth?

Can you feel your tummy muscles giving an extra kick in order to reach your high notes when you sing "you can't go wrong" and "you gulp for air"? Remember the Buzzing Bee exercises! (Page 9).

SHERLOCK'S CASE NOTES

■ Start by teaching the opening two words of the chorus "stage fright" and add an action, eg a panicky jazz hand in the rest. Then teach the remainder of the chorus.

■ In terms of diction this song is perhaps the most taxing in this book. Isolate the difficult corners, eg "You make your face, your shoulders brace, your heart is racing along" (bar 12 and 13). Practise these phrases by whispering, using silly voices and singing slowly (see Clues to unison singing page 30).

■ If your children are new to part-singing, sing the top part only where the lines divide at "Stage fright, stage fright" (bars 41 onwards), or teach the lower part at a different time to a separate group of children. (See Clues to vocal harmony, page 66.)

■ Danger point: to perfect the final phrase of the song (bar 46 to the end) listen carefully to the CD to hear the rhythm of the words "That little snake you've got". Clap twice in the rests before the word "stage", and use the rest to take a good deep breath to sing the final long "fright!"

See Me

from *Stage Songs*

performance – CD 2 track 23; backing – CD 2 track 24
starting note – D; introduction – 9 beats

Chris Williams

138

Singing Sherlock wants to know:

🔍 *Can you think about the times you have been a performer, eg in a school concert or play, before your dance exam or singing a solo?*

🔍 *How did you feel just before the performance started? Are your facial expressions reflecting your feelings as you sing?*

🔍 *Are you remembering to begin each new verse softly? Decide how much to turn your 'volume control switch' (see page 31).*

SHERLOCK'S CASE NOTES

- *Ask the children to sing the words as if they are speaking directly to another person.*

- *Do not start the song too loud, each verse needs to gather momentum gradually towards the chorus. In contrast to the verses, the chorus needs to be sung with a legato (smooth) sound and a full vocal tone.*

- *You may wish to discuss with the children different interpretations of the words "See me". For example, "I'm really scared and I can't believe it's me standing on the stage", or "I'm standing on the stage with lots of other people and I want the audience to see just me", or "Look at me, I'm centre stage! Aren't I amazing?"*

- *Danger points: in the final chorus "See me, singing all alone", ask the children to the count six beats' rest (bar 82–83), before singing "See me" which is repeated four times. These need to be sung very smoothly, and each slightly softer and slower than the previous one.*

Don't Call Us

from *Stage Songs*

performance – CD 2 track 25; backing – CD 2 track 26
starting note – C; introduction – 16 beats

Chris Williams

First, the dance and then the so-lo, Fol-lowed by an in-ter-view,

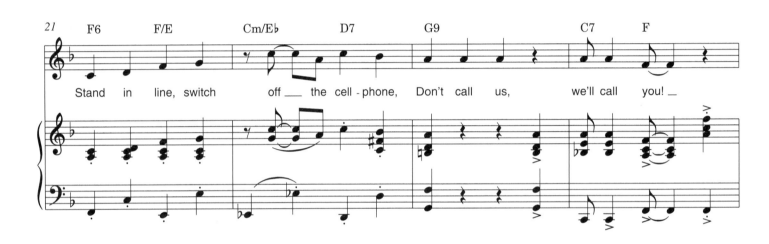

Stand in line, switch off the cell-phone, Don't call us, we'll call you!

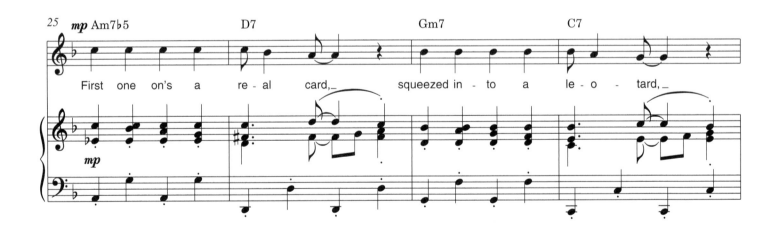

First one on's a re-al card, squeezed in-to a le-o-tard,

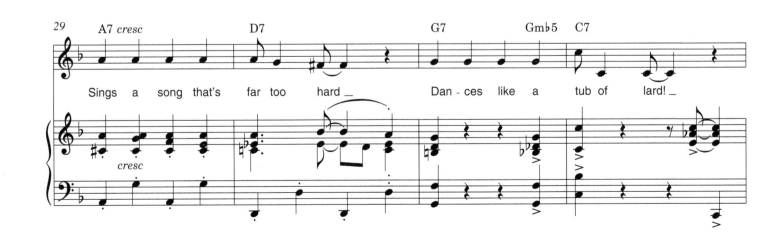

Sings a song that's far too hard Dan-ces like a tub of lard!

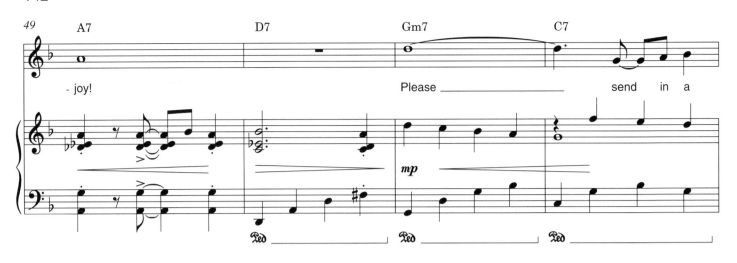

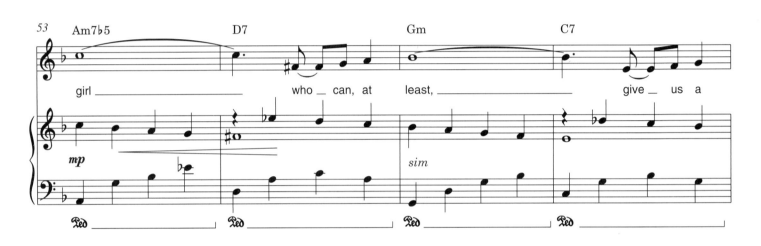

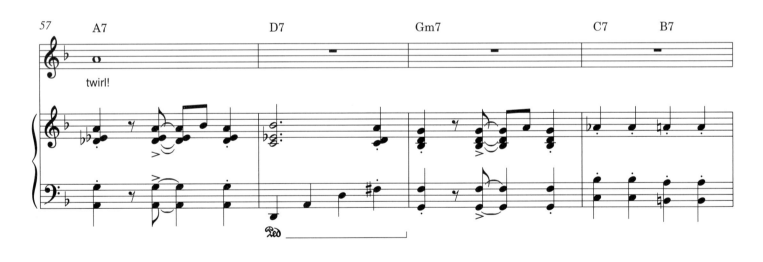

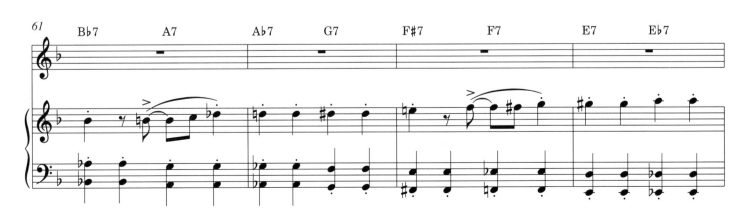

- Can you think how you might set the scene of the song in the long introduction?
- Can you make a really good telephone ring tone?
- Do you know who 'The Bard' is?
- Are you putting your lips forward to create a good, round sound on the last word "you" of the song? Are you making sure you do not slide between these notes?

SHERLOCK'S CASE NOTES

- *A very topical and humorous song that will really excite both children and audience. It is perhaps the easiest of this set of four songs.*
- *The words move very quickly from one idea to the next. The children need to constantly think ahead in order to express each new thought fully.*
- *You will need to explain the phrases "Hoisted by their own petard" and "Feels like we've been abattoired". A petard was a medieval small bomb used to blow up gates and walls when trying to capture a besieged castle. Today, the phrase to be 'hoist by one's own petard' means 'to be harmed by one's own plan to harm someone else' or 'to fall into one's own trap'. The phrase was coined by Shakespeare in the play* Hamlet.
- *Danger point: the words "Don't call us, we'll call you!" are sung three times, but each time is slightly different. Watch out for the rests the second and third time.*

In the End

from *Stage Songs*

performance – CD 2 track 27; backing – CD 2 track 28
starting note – F; introduction – 16 beats

Chris Williams

Andante (but with a swing!) ♩. = 84

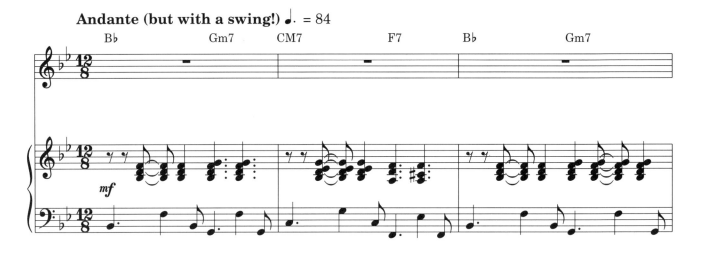

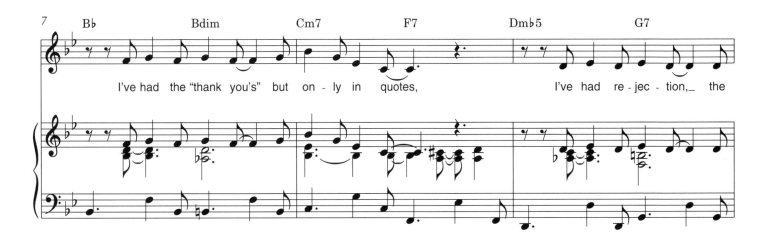

Singing Sherlock wants to know:

- *Are you using your 'posh voice' when singing "Before the concert at the Royal Albert Hall" and "I'll sing for duchesses"?*

- *Are you using your 'football match' voice when singing "They're on the pages right next to the football", as you wave your favourite team's scarf?*

- *Do you know the names of other famous musicals that are performed in the West End, London's world-famous theatreland?*

- *Are you convincing the audience to "keep their dream" and never give up?*

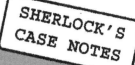

SHERLOCK'S CASE NOTES

- *This needs to have a 'show-time' swing right from the outset.*

- *At the words "sometimes I feel my career's in regression" (bar 11 and 12), be careful with the note intervals and the rhythm.*

- *The two-part singing needs some care. Make sure the children singing part 1 give the long notes their full length.*

- *The children singing part 2 should be absolutely secure with the falling chromatic notes on the words "Someday you'll see me on TV and I will be" (bar 29–33). Take care too, with the interval between the words "be" and "top" in the phrase "be top of the tree" (bar 35).*

- *The last section from "in the end, believe me baby" (bar 57 onwards), will need lots of work; the words "in the end" are repeated three times, and each time both the rhythm and melodic phrase is different. Add a finger click to help internalise the rests.*

- *You may need to explain that Cats and The Boyfriend were musicals that ran in the West End in London.*